NEW MENTAL MATHS

$\frac{25}{12} + \frac{4}{2} =$

By:
Dr. C.L. Garg, M.Sc., Ph.D.
Poonam Arora

60.3
+5.2
=65.5

56.5 +

I, II, III, IV, V

MANOJ PUBLICATIONS

Book-4

Mental Maths is being taught in primary and middle classes to enhance the mathematical aptitude of the beginners by presenting the numbers to the child as means of recreation, fun and creating inspiration. This series is written for classes I to VIII. These books peck the minds of the students without much written calculations. This exercise will encourage students to think and understand the basics of mathematics.

This volume is meant for class IV. Illustrations, symbols, pictures and patterns have been used to make the subject easy.

In writing this series of mental math books, our effort is to make mathematical problems a fun to solve by students.

The endeavour is to put principles of mathematics in easy way to help children develop interest in maths.

These books will make mathematics an enjoyable subject for children.

—*Authors*

EDITION : 2018

ISBN 978-81-310-1046-4

Printed at: Prince Print Process

Manoj Publications

761, Main Road, Burari, Delhi-110084

Phones: 91-11-27611116, 27611349, **Fax**: 27611546 (**M**) 9868112194

E-mail: info@manojpublications.com, **Website**: www.manojpublications.com

Showroom:

1583-84, Dariba Kalan, Chandni Chowk, Delhi-110006

Phones: 91-11-23262174, 23268216 (**M**) 9818753569

Contents

Tasks

Contents

Tasks

Tests

rade ◯

umerals

Write the following numerals in words.

a. 28754 twenty eight thousand seven hundred fifty four

b. 53285 fifty three thousand two hundred eighty five

c. 499910 four hundred ninety nine thousand nine hundred ten

d. 318752 three hundred eighteen thousand seven hundred fifty two

e. 920470 nine hundred thousand four hundred seventy

f. 29980 twenty nine thousand nine hundred eighty

Write the following in numbers.

a. Eighty thousand fifty four 8054

b. Seventy thousand ninety two ....

c. Nine thousand six hundred fifty two ....

d. Fifty thousand and thirty three ....

e. Sixty six thousand two hundred eleven ....

f. Six lakh eighty thousand five hundred sixty three 680,563

Write the place value of 8 in each of these numbers.

5872 .... 8732 .... 9780 ....

3581 .... 5388 .... 7398 ....

Write the place value of 9 in each of these numbers.

89532 .... 333956 ....

Complete the following series.

3272	3273	....	....	....	....
9754	9755	....	....	....	....
8210	8211	....	....	....	....
5981	5982	....	....	....	....

Grade ◯

Hindi–Arabic and Roman numerals

1. Write the Roman numerals for the following.

a.	84	g.	76 ....
b.	96	h.	110 ....
c.	102	i.	120 ....
d.	52	j.	187 ....
e.	100	k.	170 ....
f.	60	l.	200 ....

2. Write the Hindu–Arabic numerals for the following.

a.	XXXIII	g.	XCV ....
b.	XXV	h.	XCVII ....
c.	LXXIV	i.	CXXI ....
d.	LXVIII	j.	CXXIII ....
e.	XLV	k.	CV ....
f.	XLVII	l.	XCII ....

3. Fill in the boxes >, < or =

XXIV	☐	25	CXVII	☐	100+7
XXVII	☐	38	CXXV	☐	170
XCV	☐	75	XXXIX	☐	30+9
LXVII	☐	LXXI	LXXX	☐	40+40
XXII	☐	20+2	CLX	☐	200
CCXX	☐	225	CLVIII	☐	158

Grade ◯

Write in Roman numerals.

40	☐	305	☐	502	☐
52	☐	105	☐	1505	☐
100	☐	25	☐	110	☐
1000	☐	63	☐	400	☐

. Write in Hindu–Arabic numerals.

XIX	☐	MD	☐	DC	☐
CD	☐	XL	☐	MC	☐
MLX	☐	LIV	☐	CCCL	☐
MCC	☐	CXX	☐	CIX	☐

. Tick (✓) for true and (×) for false.

XX = 21	☐	CX = 110	☐	XIX = 21	☐
XL = 42	☐	LX = 50	☐	VC = 92	☐
D = 50	☐	D = 500	☐	DI = 105	☐
M = 1000	☐	M = 1000	☐	MM = 2000	☐

. Write the following in Roman numerals.

a. Your age ....

b. Your class ....

c. Last two digits of your telephone number ....

d. Your brother/sister's age ....

Grade ◯

Number system

1. Write the following in numbers.
   a. One less than the highest five digit number ....
   b. One more than the smallest three digit number ....
   c. One more than the highest four digit number ....
   d. One more than the smallest six digit number ....

2. Write > or < in the box.

3910+1	☐	3900	7070	☐	7007
4528+2	☐	4518+2	4000+400+40	☐	4400
9300	☐	9400	500+80+3	☐	583
5008	☐	508	695	☐	600+19

3. Complete the series.
   a. 23521, 23522, ..., ..., ..., ..., ...
   b. 69325, 69326, ..., ..., ..., ..., ...
   c. 41929, ..., ..., 41932, ..., ..., ...

4. Write the following numbers.
   a. The smallest 9 digit number ....
   b. The highest 7 digit number ....
   c. The highest 8 digit number ....
   d. The smallest 8 digit number ....

5. Complete the series.
   a. 2, 4, 7, 11, ..., ..., ..., ..., ..., ..., ..., ..., ...
   b. 5, 8, 12, 17, ..., ..., ..., ..., ..., ..., ..., ..., ...
   c. 12, 13, 14, 15, ..., ..., ..., ..., ..., ..., ..., ..., ...

rade ◯

scending and descending order of numbers

Write in ascending order.

a. 5431, 9287, 3214, 9000, 5100

............., ..., ..., ..., ...

b. 18754, 17851, 37921, 54900, 17700

............., ..., ..., ..., ...

c. 87549, 87000, 78080, 78000, 87500

............., ..., ..., ..., ...

Write in descending order.

a. 15493, 18780, 13540, 19300, 78570

.................., ..., ..., ..., ...

b. 3210, 3700, 4200, 3780, 4350

.................., ..., ..., ..., ...

c. 32900, 51807, 51880, 32910, 51870

.................., ..., ..., ..., ...

Solve the following.

a. $(8\times10000) + (7\times1000) + (3\times100) + (8\times 10) + 5 =$ ....

b. $(18\times1000) + (7\times100) + 12 =$ ....

c. $(5\times1000) + (6\times100) + (8\times10) + 8 =$ ....

Write the successor (next number).

5492	1870 ....
8350	2539 ....
7390	4330 ....
1583	1791 ....

ate :...................... Teacher's Signature :......................

Grade ◯

Expanded form

1. Write the expanded form of the following numbers.
   a. 73,825 ....
   b. 24,990 ....
   c. 1,00,001 ....
   d. 98,043 ....
2. Add the following to get the number.
   a. 700000+60000+300+50+7 ....
   b. 800000+5000+40+3 ....
   c. 5000+30+18 ....
   d. 400000+10000+70+4 ....
   e. 65000+500+30+8 ....
   f. 990000+80000+80+8 ....
3. Write the place value of the bigger digit in each number?

548272	973241	873425	329332
513824	32921	732432	910734
3654390	27170	32943	721081

4. Write the predecessors of the following.

.... 25938	 73590
.... 73820	 81925
.... 43819	 73940

5. Write the successors of the following.

58923	775633	445932 ....
879921	385722	672353 ....

Date :..........

Teacher's Signature :..........

Grade ◯

Task 7

dditión

dd the following.

214235 + 316368	562501 + 376168	114324 + 156284
562862 + 189872	124823 + 235766	835027 + 940536
4010261 + 3272638	405032 + 240350	2243512 + 5304672
236547 + 357105	2332658 + 4736082	4327256 + 4656026
4224378 + 4581326	2525861 + 4234587	9210532 + 3217012
9816931 + 8997651	3293409 + 3434562	1356582 + 2423442

Grade ◯

Subtraction

Subtract the following.

243742 − 188242	537649 − 425436	764789 − 560502
396438 − 221380	598796 − 287643	487657 − 353611
432493 − 321250	965674 − 123434	432725 − 365022
8496788 − 3252728	6725861 − 4369421	6547962 − 3327812
5253346 − 3132097	2257652 − 2178093	9155288 − 8670380
9875005 − 5583227	3253468 − 3195674	5278462 − 3195764
7895625 − 3212507	9876302 − 8967555	89999582 − 38999889

Date :......................

Teacher's Signature :..................

Grade ◯

Task 9

Addition and subtraction

9937677 − 9899070	267898 + 321042
840982 − 695120	7647895 + 1605034
674468 − 543234	784368 + 673143
598769 − 287432	4327526 + 4583818
6547962 − 3382167	214235 + 116808
9256463 − 6104527	314235 + 416386
8658391 − 6392286	46937253 + 82369212

Date :.......................

Teacher's Signature :.......................

Grade ◯

Addition and subtraction questions

a. The collection of wealth tax in three years is Rs. 25760, Rs. 58372 and Rs. 3000 more than the collection of first two years respectively. What is the total collection?

b. Ansh had Rs. 4000 in his pocket. He bought 3 fans for Rs. 1000 each, a pair of sandals for Rs. 259, and a belt. The money left with him is Rs. 190. What is the cost of belt?

c. A man has 360 hundred rupee notes, 448 fifty rupee notes and 118 twenty rupee notes. How much money is there in his kitty?

d. A man had Rs 1000, Rs 500 and Rs 100 with him. He spends Rs 450, how much money is left with him?

e. If Ram had Rs 5328 and spends Rs 4297 on shopping. How much is left with him?

f. You have 4 notes of Rs 1000 and 3 notes of Rs 500. How much is the total money with you?

rade

ultiplication

lve the following.

a. 234 × 400 = ...

b. 289 × 100 = ...

c. 504 × 70 = ...

d. 130 × .... = 2600

e. 504 × .... = 504

f. 865 × .... = 25950

g. 4 × 25 × 15 = ...

h. 25 × 70 × 8 = ...

i. 63 × 81 + 26 + 81 =

....

j. 766 × 99 + 766 =

....

k. .... × 1 = 65

l. 28 × 25 = 28 × (15+ ....)

m. 4 × 78 + 0 = ...

n. 2000 × 27 = ...

o. 82 × 6 = ...

p. 319 × 3 = ...

q. 11 × 11 = ...

r. 10 × 10 + 10 = ...

s. 7 × 7 + 49 = ...

t. 9836 × 8 = ...

u. 509 × 60 = ...

v. .... × 1 = 80

w. 6 × 72 + 0 = ...

x. 5 × 25 × 1 = ...

y. 10 × 10 = ...

z. 50 × 25 = ...

ate :......................

Teacher's Signature :......................

Grade

Multiplication by parts

1. Multiply 84×928

Rewrite each factor in the expanded form

84=80+4

928=900+20+8

×	900	20	8
80	72000	1600	640
4	3600	80	32
	↓ 75600	↓ 1680	↓ 672

a. 900 × 80 = 72000
b. 20 × 80 = 1600
c. 8 × 80 = 640
d. 900 × 4 = 3600
e. 20 × 4 = 80
f. 8 × 4 = 72000

Add 75600 + 1680 + 672 = 779

∴ 84 × 928 = 77952

2. Multiply following as shown in above example.

a. 36 × 529

×	500	20	9
30			
6			

b. 84 × 241

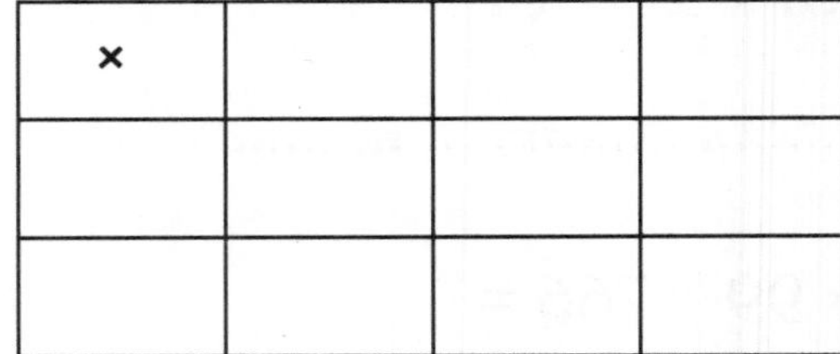

×			

c. 18 × 785

×			

d. 54 × 236

×			

rade ◯

ore on Multiplication

ultiply the following.

947 × 22	873 × 54	928 × 73
735 × 25	852 × 12	792 × 90
542 × 70	877 × 19	751 × 25
450 × 50	725 × 35	350 × 15
617 ×140	828 × 100	543 ×120

Date :......................

Teacher's Signature :......................

Grade ◯

Solve the problems

1. There are 256 pens in a box. How many pens are there in 450 such boxes?

2. A company earns Rs Nine Lakh Eighty Five Thousand Seven Hundred Seventy Seven rupees every month. What will be its earning in 12 years?

3. The cost of 9 TV sets is Rs. 89185. Find the cost of 14 such TV sets.

4. In a row 21 rose plants can be planted. How many rose plants can be planted in 112 such rows?

5. The cost of one dozen oranges is Rs 44. How much is the cost of 6 dozen of oranges?

6. The number of days in 22 weeks are.

7. The number of paise in Rs 150 are.

Grade ◯

Division

Solve the following by applying BODMAS (Bracket Off Division Multiplication Addition Subtraction)

a. 12048 ÷ 12 = ...

b. 10000 ÷ 1000 × 20 = ...

c. 257 ÷ 257 = ...

d. 4681 ÷ 1 = ...

e. .... ÷ 461 = 1

f. (768 ÷ 32) ÷ 16 = ...

g. (2×14) ÷ 28 = ...

h. 71 – 71 × (71 ÷ 7) = ...

i. 37214 ÷ 100 = Q..........., R ....

j. 54967 ÷ 50 = Q .... R ....

k. .... ÷ 149 = 0

l. 821 ÷ 821 = ...

m. 68 ÷ 12 = Q ...., R ....

n. (18 ÷ 9) + 18 = ...

o. (96 ÷ 12) + 12 = ...

p. 768 + 321 ÷ 16 = ...

q. 751 ÷ .... = 1

r. 36000 ÷ 600 = ...

s. 523 ÷ 0 = ...

t. 54000 ÷ 20 = ...

u. 112 ÷ 16 + 38 = ...

v. 216 ÷ .... = 18

w. 79 – 64 + 83 = ...

x. 93 × 0 + 98 ÷ 6 = ...

y. 12 ÷ 3 = ...

z. 15 ÷ 3 = ...

Grade ◯

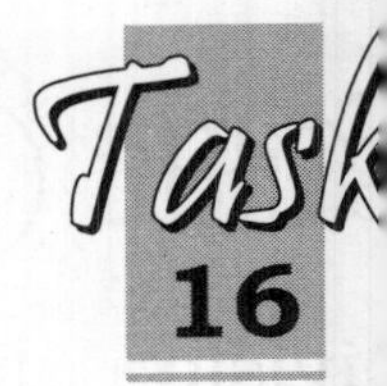

More divisions

Division with big numbers.

38) 196128 (

Q .... R...............

31) 4960 (

Q .... R...............

42) 512138 (

Q .... R...............

58) 385238 (

Q .... R...............

100) 88743 (

Q .... R...............

24) 87543 (

Q .... R...............

500) 5758 (

Q .... R...............

50) 500005 (

Q .... R...............

Date :......................

Teacher's Signature :................

Grade ◯

Division questions

Write the quotient in the boxes below.

480 ÷ 40 =	☐	490 ÷ 7 =	☐
248 ÷ 2 =	☐	600 ÷ 10 =	☐
999 ÷ 9 =	☐	999 ÷ 9 =	☐
121 ÷ 11 =	☐	550 ÷ 5 =	☐
369 ÷ 3 =	☐	330 ÷ 11 =	☐
120 ÷ 4 =	☐	150 ÷ 5 =	☐

. Find the quotient and remainder of the following.

10) 375 (

10) 473 (

Q .... R................

Q .... R................

. Put (✓) or (×) for the following.

a. 545 × 1 = 0
b. 137 × 0 = 0
c. 117 + 3 = 120
d. 243 × 1 = 243
e. 0 ÷ 5 = 0
f. 50 ÷ 1 = 10

. Number of weeks in 356 days = ...

. Number of years in 4015 days = ...

Grade ◯

Match the numbers

1. Match the equations with their correct answers. One is done for you.

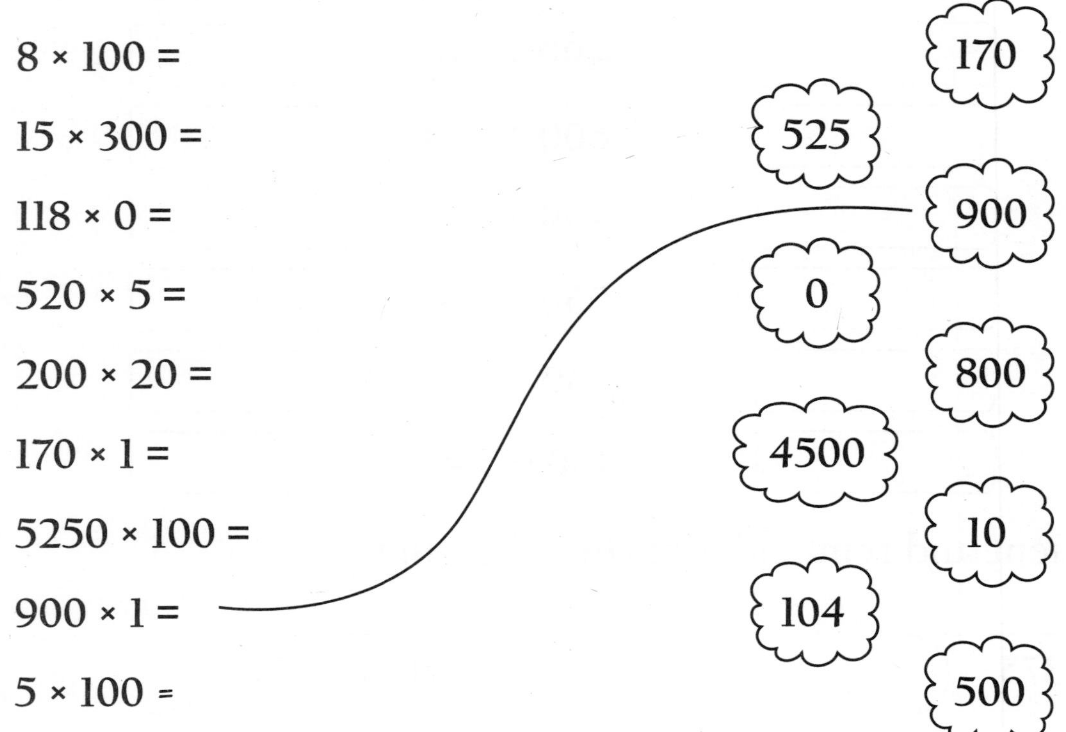

2. Multiply the following.

$$\begin{array}{r} 2840 \\ \times\ 40 \\ \hline \end{array} \qquad \begin{array}{r} 9327 \\ \times\ 27 \\ \hline \end{array} \qquad \begin{array}{r} 400 \\ \times\ 10 \\ \hline \end{array}$$

$$\begin{array}{r} 5437 \\ \times\ 135 \\ \hline \end{array} \qquad \begin{array}{r} 320 \\ \times\ 25 \\ \hline \end{array} \qquad \begin{array}{r} 3420 \\ \times\ 125 \\ \hline \end{array}$$

rade ◯

ctors

Shade only the multiples of 2 and 5.

2	3	4	5	6	7	8	9	10	
11	12	13	14	15	16	17	18	19	20
21	22	23	24	25	26	27	28	29	30
31	32	33	34	35	36	37	38	39	40
41	42	43	44	45	46	47	48	49	50
51	52	53	54	55	56	57	58	59	60

Make the factors of 12, 24, 36.

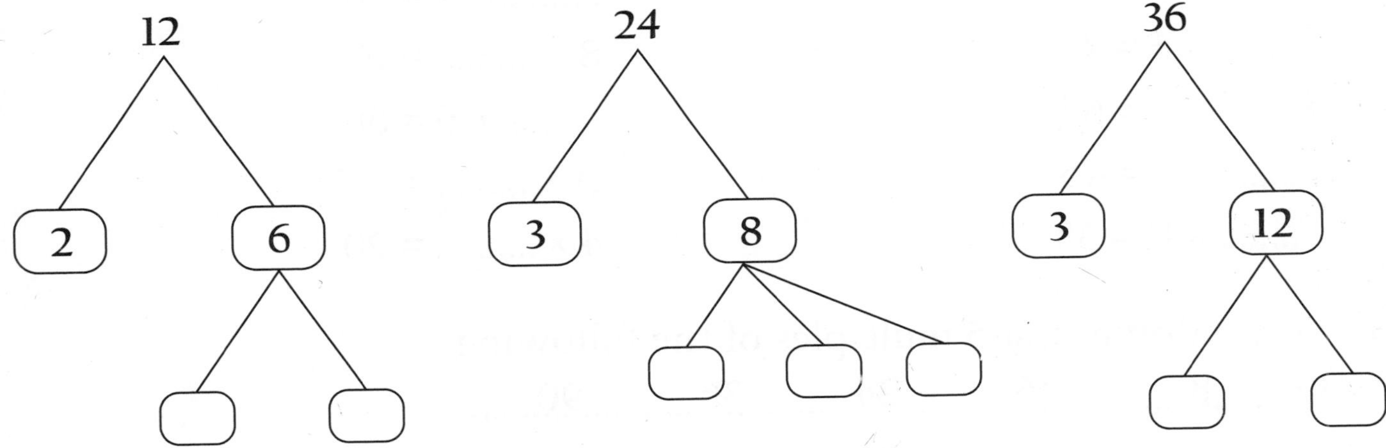

Write all factors of 12 = ...

. Write all factors of 32 = ...

. Write all factors of 36 = ...

. Write all factors of 50 = ...

. Write all factors of 64 = ...

ate :......................

Teacher's Signature :.......................

Grade

Task 20

Factors and multiples

1. Write the factors of each of the following.

2 × 4 = 8	6 = 3 × 2
3 × 5 = 15	54 = 9 × 6
8 × 2 = 16	24 = 6 × 4
18 = 9 × 2	7 × 7 = 49
2 × 4 = 25	16 = 8 × 2
22 = 2 × 11	40 = 4 × 10

2. Write the missing factors of each of the following.

8 × .... = 48	6 × .... = 30
9 × .... = 36	.... × 9 = 36
.... × 6 = 42	8 × .... = 16
8 × .... = 64	.... × 6 = 60
.... × 9 = 45	11 × .... = 55
.... × 11 = 33	4 × .... = 20

3. Write down first 5 multiples of the following.

8= ....8....... ....16...... ....24...... ....36...... ....90.......

6= ....

9= ....

12= ....

11= ....

15= ....

20= ....

30= ....

Grade ◯

Lowest common multiple

1. The multiples of 2 are 2, 4, 6, 8, 10, 12, 14, 16, 18, 20 ....

   The multiples of 4 are 4, 8, 12, 16, 20, 24, 28, 32, 36, 40 ....

   The common multiples of 2 and 4 are 4, 8, 12, 16, 20 ....

   4 is the smallest number which is common multiple of 2 and 4

   4 is called the lowest common multiple of 2 and 4

   The short form of lowest common multiple is LCM

2. Write ten multiples of each of the following pairs and find common multiples and LCM.

2 and 3	4 and 12
3 and 5	3 and 9
6 and 8	6 and 12
5 and 10	10 and 15
8 and 12	8 and 16

3. Complete the following factors of 12 and 24.

   Factors of 12 : 1 ▢ ▢ ▢ ▢ ▢ 12

   Factors of 24 : 1 ▢ ▢ ▢ ▢ ▢ ▢ 24

   a. Name the common factor of 12 and 24? ....

   b. What is the highest common factor of 12 and 24? ....

   c. What is the lowest common factor of 12 and 24? ....

   d. What are the factors of 48? ....

   e. What are factors of 24? ....

   f. What is LCM and HCF of 24 and 48? ....

Grade ◯

HCF and common factors

Find the common factors and the highest common factor.

For example, find common and highest factor of 12 and 24.

The factors of 12 are 1, 2, 3, 4, 6, 12

The factors of 24 are 1, 2, 3, 4, 6, 8, 12

The CFs of 12 and 24 are 1, 2, 3, 4, 6, 12

The HCF of 12 and 24 are 12

1. Find the HCF

6 and 18	9 and 12 ....
14 and 21	8 and 12 ....
10 and 20	18 and 32 ....
20 and 30	16 and 20 ....
24 and 36	12 and 15 ....

2. Encircle the numbers which are factors of 32.

   3, 4, 9, 10, 16, 20

3. Fill in the blanks.

   a. The factors of 4 are .... and ....

   b. The only factor of 1 is ....

   c. 10 is multiple of 2 ....

   d. The product of 8 and 6 is ....

   e. The product of 7 and 5 is ....

   f. 27 is the .... of 9 and 3

   g. .... is a factor of every number

4. Find HCF of 8 and 16.

5. Find HCF of 10 and 20.

Date :......................

Teacher's Signature :......................

rade ◯

en and Odd numbers

Nrite E for even and O for odd numbers.

15 ☐ 24 ☐ 30 ☐ 17 ☐

19 ☐ 50 ☐ 81 ☐ 88 ☐

Write even numbers between 30 and 44 ....

Write odd numbers between 21 and 35 ....

The first five even multiples of 7 are ....

The first five odd multiples of 9 are ....

Write down the factors of 54 ....

All factors of 75 ....

The first five multiples of 12 ....

The first three common multiples of 4 and 5 ....

The product of 13 and 5 is ....

The product of 9 and 6 is ....

The product of 15 and 7 is ....

The product of 9 and 5 is ....

The product of 7 and 8 is ....

Grade ◯

Rounding the numbers

1. Round the following numbers to the nearest of 10.

53	128 ....
82	185 ....
102	205 ....
115	295 ....
120	352 ....

2. Round the following numbers to the nearest of 100.

678	575 ....
332	627 ....
561	225 ....
356	444 ....
527	325 ....

3. Round the following numbers to the nearest of 1000.

1299	3702 ....
1822	1629 ....
1651	1872 ....
2996	3727 ....
5392	3928 ....

rade ◯

ldition and subtraction by rounding the numbers

Actual Sum	Estimated Sum
3652 + 6811	
9873 + 4921	
2864 + 9201	

Actual Difference	Estimated Difference
7276 − 5721	
3573 − 1976	
7283 − 3729	

ate :.....................

Teacher's Signature :.......................

Grade ◯

Fractions

A division of number is called fraction. For example, half of an apple is calle 1/2. Similarly 50 paisa coin is 50/100 = 1/2 and 25 paisa coin is 25/100 = 1/4 of rupee. Like that most of the things form fractions.

Improper fraction is a mixed number. A mixed number is the sum of a who number and a proper fraction. *For example,*

Mixed fraction = $1\frac{3}{8}$ Improper fraction = $\frac{11}{8}$ Proper fraction = $\frac{5}{8}$

If two fractions are equal they are called like fractions. $\frac{2}{3} = \frac{4}{6} = \frac{6}{9}$ etc.

1. Change to mixed numbers.

   $\frac{8}{5}$, $\frac{11}{6}$, $\frac{9}{7}$ etc.

2. Change to improper fractions.

   $1\frac{1}{3}$, $2\frac{1}{5}$, $4\frac{2}{5}$ etc.

3. Changed mixed to improper fractions.

   $1\frac{3}{8} = \frac{11}{8}$ $10\frac{2}{8} =$ ....

   $5\frac{2}{11} =$ .... $3\frac{2}{5} =$ ....

   $1\frac{1}{9} =$ .... $5\frac{2}{3} =$ ....

4. Change improper to mixed fractions.

   $\frac{8}{3} = 2\frac{2}{3}$ $\frac{12}{5} =$ .... $\frac{7}{5} =$ .... $\frac{8}{3} =$ .....

ɜrade ◯

ike and unlike fractions

Encircle only the like fractions.

$\frac{2}{6}$ $\frac{1}{9}$ $\frac{2}{8}$ $\frac{5}{6}$ $\frac{7}{6}$ $\frac{3}{5}$ $\frac{8}{6}$

$\frac{11}{12}$ $\frac{14}{12}$ $\frac{9}{14}$ $\frac{7}{15}$ $\frac{8}{12}$ $\frac{15}{17}$ $\frac{0}{0}$

$\frac{8}{3}$ $\frac{9}{4}$ $\frac{7}{3}$ $\frac{1}{5}$ $\frac{5}{3}$ $\frac{6}{4}$ $\frac{8}{3}$

. Fill in the oval with < or >.

$\frac{7}{3}$ ◯ $\frac{5}{4}$	$\frac{9}{2}$ ◯ $\frac{10}{1}$
$\frac{2}{6}$ ◯ $\frac{5}{3}$	$\frac{5}{7}$ ◯ $\frac{7}{5}$
$\frac{6}{5}$ ◯ $\frac{4}{5}$	$\frac{6}{3}$ ◯ $\frac{8}{4}$
$\frac{5}{8}$ ◯ $\frac{4}{6}$	$\frac{9}{3}$ ◯ $\frac{7}{5}$

Fill in the blanks.

$\frac{3}{4} = \frac{15}{\square}$	$\frac{4}{5} = \frac{12}{\square}$	$\frac{5}{8} = \frac{\square}{16}$
$\frac{8}{7} = \frac{64}{\square}$	$\frac{7}{6} = \frac{35}{\square}$	$\frac{5}{7} = \frac{\square}{21}$
$\frac{5}{9} = \frac{\square}{45}$	$\frac{8}{5} = \frac{\square}{40}$	$\frac{8}{3} = \frac{9}{\square}$

Grade ◯

Ascending and Descending fractions

1. Arrange the following in ascending order.

$\frac{5}{9}, \frac{10}{9}, \frac{8}{9}, \frac{12}{9}$

$\frac{7}{12}, \frac{5}{12}, \frac{3}{12}, \frac{1}{12}, \frac{8}{12}$

$\frac{6}{14}, \frac{5}{14}, \frac{9}{14}, \frac{12}{14}, \frac{3}{14}$

$\frac{1}{3}, \frac{1}{4}, \frac{1}{2}, \frac{1}{5}$

$\frac{2}{3}, \frac{3}{5}, \frac{4}{7}, \frac{5}{8}$

2. Arrange the following in descending order.

$\frac{3}{5}, \frac{4}{5}, \frac{8}{5}, \frac{6}{5}$

$\frac{5}{10}, \frac{2}{10}, \frac{8}{10}, \frac{7}{10}, \frac{12}{10}$

$\frac{1}{5}, \frac{1}{8}, \frac{1}{4}, \frac{1}{6}$

3. Write equivalent fractions for each of the following.

$\frac{1}{5}$ = — = — $\frac{3}{5}$ = — = —

$\frac{4}{6}$ = — = — $\frac{4}{7}$ = — = —

rade ◯

ldition and subtraction of fractions

Add like terms

$\frac{5}{9} + \frac{5}{7} =$ ☐

$\frac{5}{4} + \frac{3}{4} =$ ☐

$\frac{9}{5} + \frac{6}{5} =$ ☐

$\frac{16}{3} + \frac{4}{3} =$ ☐

$\frac{15}{8} + \frac{4}{8} =$ ☐

$\frac{5}{8} + \frac{5}{8} + \frac{3}{8} =$ ☐

$\frac{7}{15} + \frac{5}{15} + \frac{3}{15} =$ ☐

Subtract like terms

$\frac{7}{5} - \frac{3}{5} =$ ☐

$\frac{18}{6} + \frac{4}{6} =$ ☐

$\frac{9}{3} + \frac{7}{3} =$ ☐

$\frac{18}{6} + \frac{5}{6} =$ ☐

$\frac{20}{5} + \frac{5}{5} =$ ☐

$\frac{13}{14} + \frac{4}{14} =$ ☐

$\frac{14}{15} + \frac{7}{15} =$ ☐

Add the following

$1\frac{2}{3} + 3\frac{2}{3} + 4\frac{1}{3} =$ ....

$4\frac{3}{5} + 2\frac{1}{5} + 3\frac{2}{5} =$ ....

$1\frac{5}{9} + 3\frac{4}{9} + 4\frac{2}{9} =$ ....

Subtract the following

$3\frac{5}{8} - 2\frac{3}{8} =$ ....

$9\frac{1}{7} - 4\frac{2}{7} =$ ....

$11\frac{7}{11} - 5\frac{5}{11} =$ ....

Grade ◯

Addition of unlike fractions

$4\frac{2}{5} + 7\frac{1}{10} =$ ....

$3\frac{5}{7} + 2\frac{1}{14} =$ ....

$4\frac{2}{11} + 3\frac{5}{22} =$ ....

$5\frac{3}{11} + 3\frac{4}{3} =$ ....

$3\frac{1}{7} + 4\frac{3}{14} =$ ....

$5\frac{2}{5} + 3\frac{2}{15} =$ ....

$3\frac{1}{4} + 7\frac{2}{8} =$ ....

$7\frac{4}{14} + 4\frac{8}{21} =$ ....

$8 + 9\frac{2}{3} =$ ....

$4\frac{1}{3} + 2\frac{2}{9} =$ ....

$5\frac{2}{9} + 3\frac{4}{3} =$ ....

$8\frac{1}{7} + 7\frac{1}{14} =$ ....

$5\frac{2}{5} + 7\frac{3}{10} =$ ....

$7\frac{3}{22} + 4\frac{8}{33} =$ ....

$\frac{3}{6} + \frac{7}{3} =$ ....

$1\frac{1}{4} + 2\frac{3}{4} =$ ....

$\frac{8}{7} + \frac{3}{7} =$ ....

$3\frac{1}{7} + 2\frac{1}{7} =$ ....

$\frac{9}{2} + \frac{5}{6} =$ ....

$4\frac{1}{5} + 3\frac{2}{15} =$ ....

Date :......................

Teacher's Signature :................

Grade ◯

ubtraction of unlike fractions

$5\frac{9}{8} - 2\frac{3}{8} =$ ....

$9\frac{2}{11} - 1\frac{3}{11} =$ ....

$5\frac{4}{3} - 3\frac{3}{3} =$ ....

$3\frac{1}{3} - 2\frac{1}{3} =$ ....

$9\frac{2}{3} - \frac{7}{9} =$ ....

$5\frac{1}{3} - \frac{5}{6} =$ ....

$8\frac{2}{6} - 2\frac{5}{4} =$ ....

$3\frac{5}{6} - 1\frac{4}{3} =$ ....

$18 - 8\frac{2}{5} =$ ....

$4 - \frac{1}{7} =$ ....

$\frac{7}{6} - \frac{6}{4} =$ ....

$\frac{7}{11} - \frac{3}{11} =$ ....

$3\frac{5}{9} - 1\frac{9}{6} =$ ....

$5\frac{4}{9} - 3\frac{1}{3} =$ ....

$\frac{5}{2} - \frac{8}{10} =$ ....

$\frac{3}{5} - \frac{1}{5} =$ ....

$8\frac{2}{8} - \frac{5}{4} =$ ....

$4\frac{1}{3} - 1\frac{1}{6} =$ ....

$1\frac{7}{6} - 1\frac{5}{2} =$ ....

$2\frac{1}{5} - 1\frac{2}{5} =$ ....

Date :........................ Teacher's Signature :......................

Grade ◯

Multiplication of fractions

1. Multiply the following.

$\frac{2}{3} \times 6 =$ ....

$6 \times \frac{1}{5} =$ ....

$\frac{7}{8} \times 6 =$ ....

$5 \times \frac{2}{5} =$ ....

$8 \times \frac{7}{3} =$ ....

$3 \times \frac{7}{2} =$ ....

$5 \times \frac{2}{4} =$ ....

$\frac{5}{4} \times 6 =$ ....

$\frac{2}{7} \times 3 =$ ....

$\frac{3}{5} \times \frac{4}{7} =$ ....

2. Find the value of

$\frac{1}{2}$ of 12 = ...

$\frac{4}{8}$ of 40 = ...

$\frac{3}{5}$ of 20 = ...

$\frac{6}{9}$ of 81 = ...

$\frac{2}{5}$ of 40 = ...

$\frac{8}{6}$ of 54 = ...

$\frac{5}{6}$ of 30 = ...

$\frac{5}{5}$ of 25 = ...

$\frac{7}{4}$ of 28 = ...

$\frac{7}{2}$ of 28 = ...

Date :......................

Teacher's Signature :..................

Grade ◯

Fraction figures

1. Fill in the boxes.

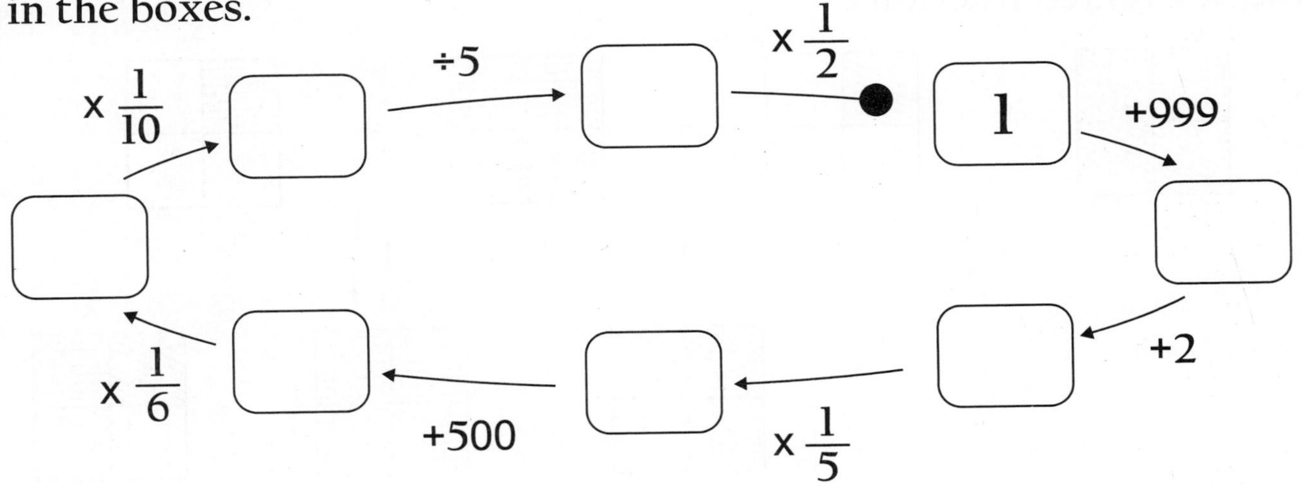

2. Add fractions.

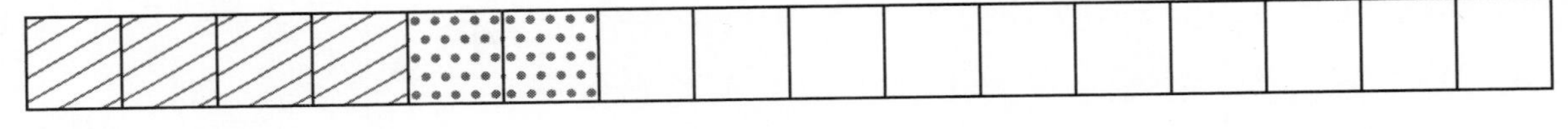

$\frac{4}{16} + \frac{2}{16} =$

3. Count and add the shaded fractions.

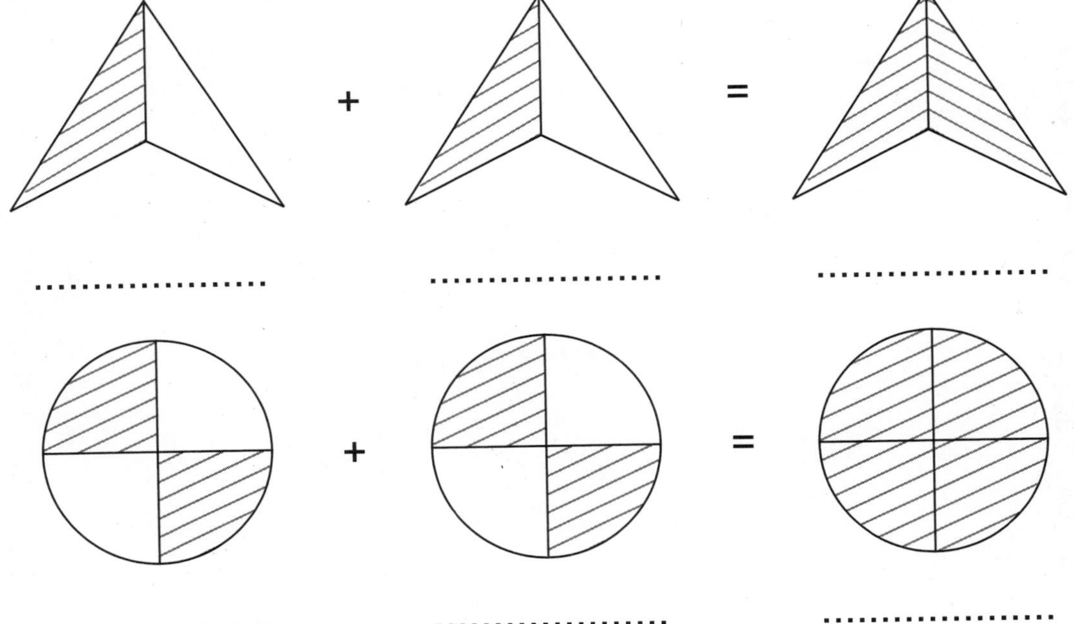

Date :......................

Teacher's Signature :......................

Grade

Shaded fractions

1. Add the mixed fractions.

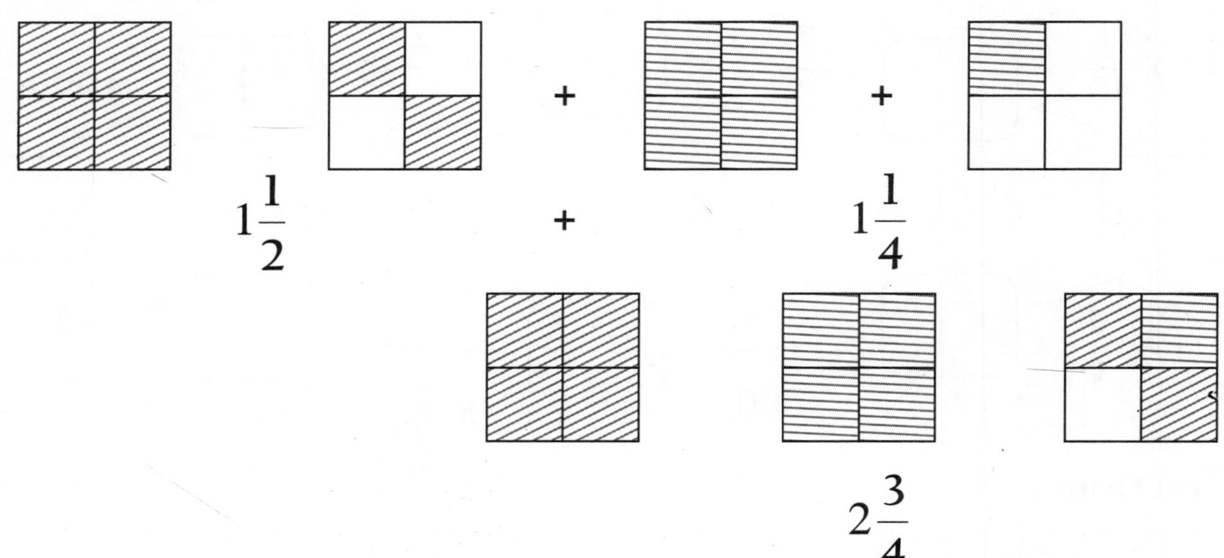

$2\frac{3}{4}$

2. Represent the following fractions through figures. One is done for you.

$1\frac{3}{4} + 1\frac{1}{2} = 3\frac{1}{4}$

$1\frac{1}{2} + 1\frac{3}{4} =$

$1\frac{1}{4} + 1\frac{1}{2} =$

$2\frac{1}{4} + 1\frac{1}{4} =$

$2\frac{1}{2} + 1\frac{3}{4} =$

rade ◯

ecimal

Write the following as common fractions and as decimal fractions.

Numbers	Common Fractions	Decimal Fraction Form
a. Seven–tenth	$\frac{7}{10}$	0.7
b. Two and four tenth		
c. Five and zero tenth		
d. Seven and four tenth		
e. Nineteen and seven tenth		
f. Four and four tenth		
g. Eight tenth		
h. Eleven hundredths		

. Complete the following.

7.9 = ...0.......... Tens ....7.......... Ones ....9.......... Tenths

49.7= .... Tens .... Ones .... Tenths

77.7= .... Tens .... Ones .... Tenths

28.7= .... Tens .... Ones .... Tenths

55.4= .... Tens .... Ones .... Tenths

17.7= .... Tens .... Ones .... Tenths

34.9= .... Tens .... Ones .... Tenths

77.6= .... Tens .... Ones .... Tenths

Date :......................

Teacher's Signature :......................

Grade ◯

Questions on decimal

1. Write the following fractions as decimal fractions.

$7\frac{3}{10}$ ______	$8\frac{3}{10}$ ______
$9\frac{2}{12}$ ______	$9\frac{7}{10}$ ______
$8\frac{7}{10}$ ______	$8\frac{2}{10}$ ______
$4\frac{3}{10}$ ______	$23\frac{7}{10}$ ______
$3\frac{1}{100}$ ______	$15\frac{3}{100}$ ______

2. Write the following as common fractions.

0.9 ______	15.9 ______
8.7 ______	28.7 ______
7.5 ______	52.3 ______
11.9 ______	5.8 ______
18.7 ______	19.7 ______
15.5 ______	25.77 ______
21.88 ______	22.75 ______

Date :......................

Teacher's Signature :......................

Grade ◯

ecimal: Greater and less than and equal to

Put > or < or = in the following.

8.5	☐	7.0	15.8	☐	15.8
18.3	☐	28.3	17.3	☐	13.8
15.9	☐	1.7	10.3	☐	10.3
10.7	☐	10.7	1.9	☐	10.9
3.7	☐	2.6	1.5	☐	1.5

Write as decimals.

$7\frac{3}{10}$	= 7.☐	$15\frac{}{10}$	= 15.8
$13\frac{2}{}$	= 13.2	$37\frac{8}{}$	= 37.8
$8\frac{9}{10}$	= 8.☐	☐ $\frac{5}{10}$	= 19.5
$17\frac{}{10}$	= 17.5	☐ $\frac{9}{10}$	= 10.9
$9\frac{1}{100}$	= ☐	$5\frac{1}{10}$	= 5.☐
$17\frac{3}{100}$	= 17.☐	$7\frac{3}{100}$	= 7.☐

Grade ◯

Decimal: Tenths and hundredths

1. Complete the following.

a. 0.18 = 1 tenth and 8 hundredth = $\frac{18}{100}$

b. 0.98 = ... tenth and hundredth =

c. 0.54 = ... tenth and .... hundredths=

d. 0.35 = ... tenth and .... hundredth =

e. 0.95 = ... tenth and .... hundredth =

f. 0.46 = ... tenth and .... hundredth =

g. 0.38 = ... tenth and .... hundredth =

h. 0.25 = ... tenth and .... hundredth =

2. Write the fractions.

3.92 =

3.52 =

7.52 =

5.73 =

1.02 =

8.1 =

1.1 =

3.2 =

8.25 =

7.35 =

9.75 =

3.12 =

4.85 =

7.25 =

8.38 =

5.35 =

rade ◯

:cimal: Addition and subtraction

Add the following.

18.75 + 10.03	15.21 + 11.21	43.75 + 19.20
73.80 + 41.21	54.30 + 18.70	81.51 + 21.50
93.40 + 11.34	82.15 + 11.13	97.19 + 11.11

Subtract the following.

52.84 − 21.12	93.15 − 21.02	73.70 − 54.25
82.70 − 51.12	57.35 − 40.15	81.75 − 35.29
38.75 − 17.25	49.23 − 17.87	30.42 − 25.28

ıte :......................

Teacher's Signature :......................

Grade ◯

Task 40

Mixed numerals

1. **Write the following as mixed numerals.**

For example: $3.56 = 3\frac{56}{100}$, $25.8 = 25\frac{8}{10}$

4.23 =	1.07 =	19.18 =
7.93 =	15.5 =	4.72 =
13.3 =	7.05 =	18.06 =
15.8 =	25.68 =	60.7 =
45.7 =	32.52 =	12.75 =

2. **Write the following in decimals.**

$7 + \frac{3}{10} + \frac{5}{100} =$

$7 + \frac{8}{10} + \frac{5}{100} =$

$2 + \frac{1}{10} + \frac{7}{100} =$

$2 + \frac{7}{100} =$

$70 + 5 + \frac{2}{100} =$

$7 + \frac{5}{10} + \frac{5}{10} =$

$90 + 2 + \frac{4}{10} =$

$3 + \frac{9}{100} =$

$7 + 8 + \frac{4}{10} =$

$5 + 2 + \frac{7}{100} =$

rade ◯

ngth measurement

What is a better unit to measure the following in cm, m or km?

a. Length of a 10 rupee note= ....

b. Distance the school bus travels= ....

c. Length of a river= ....

d. Height of a flagpole= ....

e. Length of a straw= ....

f. Height of a giraffe= ....

g. Length of a needle = ...

h. Distance from the earth to moon = ...

i. Height of a person = ...

j. Distance from Mumbai to Pune = ...

Express in metres.

a. 300 cm= ....

b. 148 cm= ....

c. 500 cm= ....

d. 8829 cm= ....

e. 1210 cm= ....

Express in kilometres.

a. 3505 m= ....

b. 55160 m= ....

c. 15800 m= ....

d. 7000 m= ....

ate :......................

Teacher's Signature :......................

Grade ◯

Length measurement questions

1. Fill up the blanks.

   a. 4785 cm = ... m .... cm.

   b. .... m = 5 km, 78 cm.

   c. 8754 m = ... km .... m.

   d. 7485 m = ... km .... m.

   e. 3 m – 2 m, 75 cm = ...

   f. 3735 km = ... m .... cm.

2. Subtract and add the following.

	km	m	cm
	330 km	818 m	89 cm
–	12 km	989 m	92 cm

	km	m	cm
	30 km	837 m	92 cm
–	17 km	794 m	87 cm

	km	m	cm
	5 km	90 m	77 cm
	7 km	81 m	13 cm
	7 km	23 m	65 cm
+	19 km	44 m	97 cm

	km	m	cm
	1 km	70 m	32 cm
	6 km	18 m	41 cm
	3 km	14 m	46 cm
+	14 km	08 m	82 cm

3. a. 15800 cm = ... m.

   b. 89001 m = ... cm.

4. Fill in the boxes with <, > or =.

   a. 8 cm ☐ 5 cm　　b. 81 cm ☐ 81 cm

   c. 112 m ☐ 115 m　　d. 127 cm ☐ 27 cm

rade ◯

Veight measurement

How much is :

a. 3kg, 250 g = ... g.

b. 1006 g = ... kg .... g.

c. 6000 kg = ... kg .... g.

d. 3 kg = ... g.

e. 200569 g = ... kg .... g.

Add and subtract.

	kg	g
	12 kg	600 g
+	11 kg	80 g

	kg	g
	47 kg	190 g
−	19 kg	60 g

	kg	g
	81 kg	880 g
+	489 kg	989 g

	kg	g
	935 kg	872 g
−	924 kg	988 g

Greater > or smaller <.

58 kg ☐ 54 kg   69 g ☐ 75 g

42 kg ☐ 57 kg   93 g ☐ 72 g

Fill in the blanks.

a. 1 kg weight balances 2 weights of .... grams.

b. 1 kg weight balances .... weights of 200 grams.

c. 1 kg weight balances 20 weights .... of gram.

d. 1 kg weight balances .... weights of 250 gm.

Grade ◯

Length and weight

Questions based on length and weight.

1. Find the least number of bags needed to hold 7800 kg of rice, if each bag can hold 65 kg of rice.

2. Abdul cover 2 km 333 m on foot and 14 km 832 m by bus. Find the total distance covered.

3. An athlete ran around a rectangular field 5 times whose length and depth are 50 m and 30 m respectively. Total distance covered by the athlete is?

4. In 200 m race, Rohit could run only for 75 m 20 cm. The distance left was?

5. A play ground is 500 m × 30 m in size. A runner ran 4 rounds in 30 minutes. How much distance he covered?

6. How much wire is needed for fencing a field whose length is 150 m and breadth is 90 m?

Grade ◯

apacity

Change the following.

a. 3000 *ml* = ... *l*

b. 45 *l* = ... *ml*

c. 191200 *ml* = ... *l*

d. 120 *l* = ... *ml*

e. 500050 *ml* = ... *l*

f. 3952 *ml* = ... *l*

g. 8250 *ml* = ... *l*

h. 202050 *ml* = ... *l*

i. 42 *l* = ... *ml*

j. 9250 *ml* = ... *l*

k. 325 *ml* = ... *l*

l. 33 *l* = ... *ml*

Add the following.

	l	*ml*
	125 *l*	300 *ml*
	52 *l*	525 *ml*
+	81 *l*	125 *ml*

	l	*ml*
	230 *l*	560 *ml*
	800 *l*	950 *ml*
+	301 *l*	860 *ml*

Subtract the following.

	l	*ml*
	92 *l*	450 *ml*
−	80 *l*	560 *ml*

	l	*ml*
	191 *l*	750 *ml*
−	187 *l*	890 *ml*

A tank has 27 *l* of water from which 18 *l* was consumed. How much was left?

A car can go 600 km with 35 *l* of petrol. How long it can go with 55 *l* of petrol?

A truck goes 500 km with 45 *l* of diesel. How long it will go with 75 *l* of diesel?

Grade ◯

Money

1. Calculate the total amount of money.

Rs. 50	Rs. 20	Rs. 10	Rs. 5	Rs. 1	50 P.	25 P.	10 P.	Total
	1	1	1			1	1	Rs. 35.35/
1	1			1	1	1		
	1	1	1	2	1	1		
2	1	1				1	1	
	2	1	1	3	1	1		
	1	2	1	4	1	1	1	

2. How many 50 rupee notes are there in 7000? ....

3. Equal the amount of money shows using the least possible number of notes and coins:

Amount	Rs. 50	Rs. 20	Rs. 10	Rs. 5	Rs. 2	Rs. 1	50 P.	25 P.	10 P.
Rs. 13.75			1		1	1	1	1	
Rs. 55.25									
Rs. 30.75									
Rs. 82.35									
Rs. 76.10									
Rs. 90.50									
Rs. 100.75									

4. How many rupees are there in 11 notes of Rs. 1000? ....

5. How many 20 rupee notes are there in Rs. 500? ....

Date :.......................

Teacher's Signature :......................

Grade

Task 47

Money: Addition and subtraction

Addition

360.00 + 315.00	124.20 + 78.80	421.10 + 88.60
144.00 + 72.25	125.00 + 63.70	255.00 + 55.40
237.25 + 122.00	745.20 + 32.40	245.20 + 47.90

Subtraction

360.55 − 235.00	121.20 − 99.40	160.00 − 75.25
156.00 − 144.30	156.75 − 120.00	250.25 − 240.00
132.82 − 120.79	159.75 − 156.75	282.00 − 128.00

Grade

Money: Multiplication and division

1. 12.50 × 3 = ______ 17.50 × 10 = ______ 9.75 × 25 = ______

2. If the cost of one hat is Rs. 23.75 what is the cost of 5 hats?

3. What will be the cost of 10 trucks if the cost of one truck is 266685?

4. Six boxes cost Rs. 223.50. What is the cost of 11 boxes?

5. Divide

6) 237.60 (

9) 987.52 (

7) 187.50 (

10) 543.80 (

Grade ◯

un time with money

How much money is left after the payment?

a.

Notebook	Rs. 10
Pen	Rs. 10
Pencil	Rs. 5
Eraser	Rs. 3
File	Rs. 20
Total	

You have	Rs. 100
Money left	

b.

Jeans	Rs. 250
Top	Rs. 150
Necklace	Rs. 50
Earings	Rs. 50
Total	

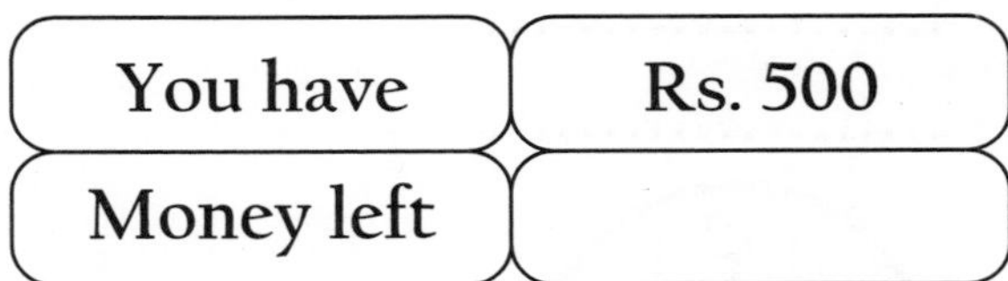

You have	Rs. 500
Money left	

One dozen pens cost Rs. 144. What will be the cost of 10 such pens?

If I spent Rs. 100 on a wallet and Rs. 150 on a bag. How much money did I have if I was left with Rs. 90?

. The cost of 5 kg. of sugar is Rs. 90. What will be the cost of 8 kg of sugar?

Grade

Time

Write the time in two ways. One is done for you.

4:40

20 min. to 5

Date :......................

Teacher's Signature :...................

ɪrade ◯

ime (A.M. and P.M.)

Write the time in A.M. or P.M. One is done for you.

a. 3:30 in the evening is 3.30 P.M.

b. 5:10 in the morning is ....

c. 7:15 in the morning is ....

d. 1.30 in the afternoon is ....

e. 9.30 in the night is ....

f. 7 O' clock in the morning is ....

g. 12 noon at noon time is ....

Fill in the blanks using A.M. or P.M.

a. I go to school at 7:30 ....

b. The sun rises at 5.30 ....

c. I go to play at 6:00 ....

d. My sister goes to bed at 10:00 ....

e. My mother cooks dinner at 9:00 ....

f. I eat my breakfast at 7:45 ....

g. The sun sets at 6.30 .... today

Write equivalent to 24 hour clock.

a. 2:45 pm ....

b. 7:30 am ....

c. 8:00 pm ....

d. 11:30 pm ....

Write equivalent to 12 hour clock.

a. 8 O' clock in the morning ....

b. 3 O' clock afternoon ....

c. 11 O' clock night ....

Teacher's Signature :.......................

Grade ◯

More questions on time

1. How many hours are there in between.
   a. 11 A.M. and 3 P.M. ....
   b. 6 P.M. and 7 A.M. ....
   c. 7 P.M. and 12 P.M. ....
   d. 5 A.M. and 2 P.M. ....
   e. 9 P.M. and 12 P.M. ....

2. What is the time? Use A.M. or P.M.
   a. 10 minutes after 4.45 A.M. ....
   b. 20 minutes after 3:30 P.M. ....
   c. 15 minutes after 12:15 P.M. ....
   d. 60 minutes after 6:00 P.M. ....
   e. One hour before 11 O' clock ....

3. Fill in the blanks.
   a. In summer sun rises at 5:30 .... A.M./P.M.
   b. In summer sun sets at 6:30 .... A.M./P.M.
   c. 12 midnight is written as .... 0000 hours/A.M./P.M.

4. a. 15 minutes to 9 is written as ....
   b. 12 in the day is written as .... noon/A.M./P.M.
   c. 25 minutes to 7 is written as ....
   d. 10 minutes to 10 is written as ....

Date :......................

Teacher's Signature :..................

Grade ◯

Calendar

Answer the following.

a. 60 seconds = ... minute

b. 60 minutes = ... hour

c. 24 hours = ... day

d. 7 days = ... week

e. 4 week = ... month

f. 12 months = ... year

g. 365/366 days = ... year

h. 1 year = ... weeks

i. Leap year comes in after every = ... years

Fill in the blanks.

a. Out of 1975, 1978, 1966, 1964, 1889 and 1905 the leaps years were ....

b. May has .... days.

c. The months with 31 days are ....

d. 12 week = ... days.

e. The month with neither 31 days or 30 days is ....

f. 6 years= ☐ months

g. 5 minutes= ☐ seconds

h. 5 days= ☐ hours

i. 1 hour= ☐ seconds

Grade ◯

Questions on Calendar

1. See in the calendar and fill in the blanks.

JANUARY 2007

sun	mon	tue	wed	thu	fri	sat
		1	2	3	4	5
6	7	8	9	10	11	12
13	14	15	16	17	18	19
20	21	22	23	24	25	26
27	28	29	30	31		

a. The number of Sundays in January 2007 were ....

b. The number of Saturdays in January 2007 were ....

c. The last day of January 2007 fall on ....

d. The first day of February 2007 was fall on ....

e. How many days February had in 2007 ....

2. Encircle the leap years in the following.

2004 2009 1995 2001 2008 2016

3. If the first Sunday in August falls on 2nd then when other Sundays will fall? ....

4. How much is the difference between a leap year and an ordinary year? ....

5. How many days are there in February of the leap year?....................................

6. If Rajat is born on 29th Feb, how many birthdays he will have in 100 years? ....

rade ◯

raphs

Comic Books	📖 📖 📖 📖 📖
Sports Magazines	📖 📖 📖 📖
Business Magazines	📖
Story Books	📖 📖 📖
Novels	📖 📖

One 📖 represents → 10 Books

By reading the graph given above answer the following questions.

a. Number of comic books. ....

b. How many sports magazines are there? ....

c. The difference between comic books and sports magazines? ....

d. Which is more—comics books or novels and how many? ....

e. Which is more—novels or business magazines? ....

Fill in the boxes.

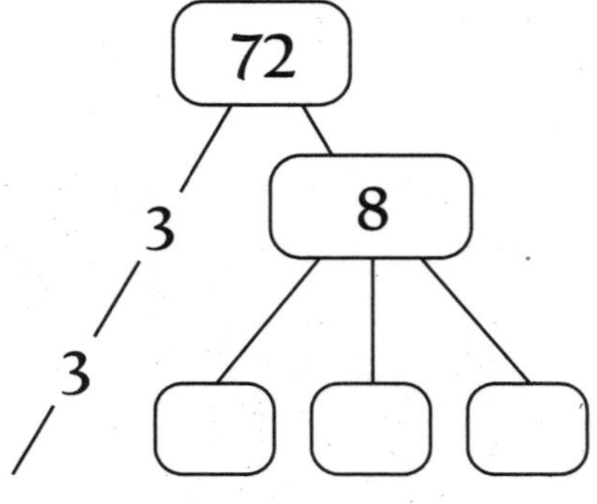

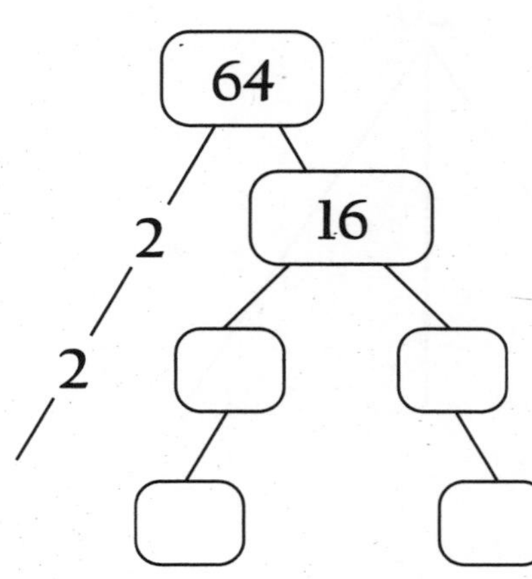

Grade ◯

Fun time with magic squares

1. An example of magic square is given for you. Fill in the remaining squares so that the total of figures (vertically and horizontally) match with total marked against each.

4	9	2
3	5	7
8	1	6

Total = 15

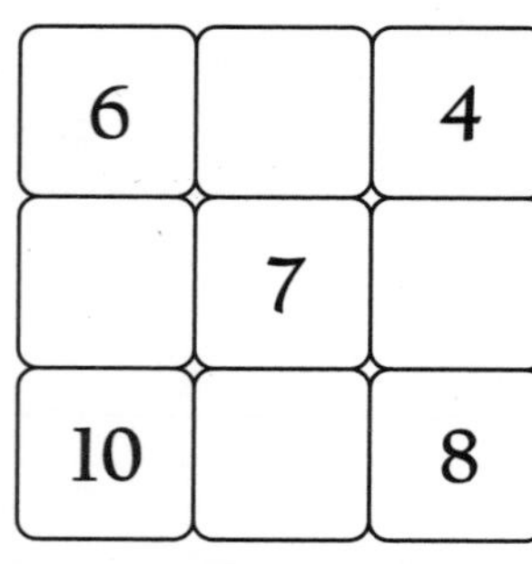

Total = 21

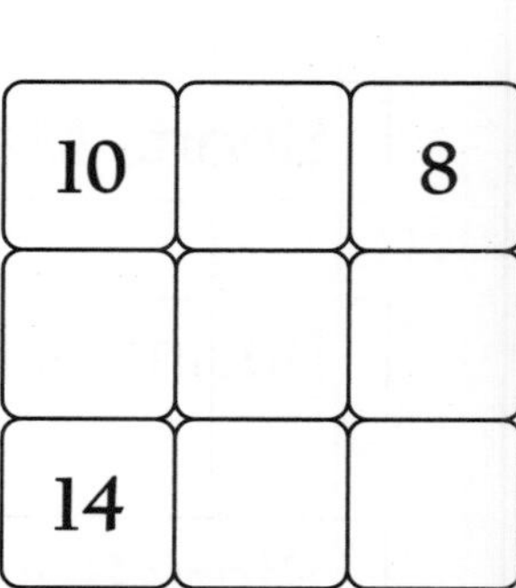

Total = 33

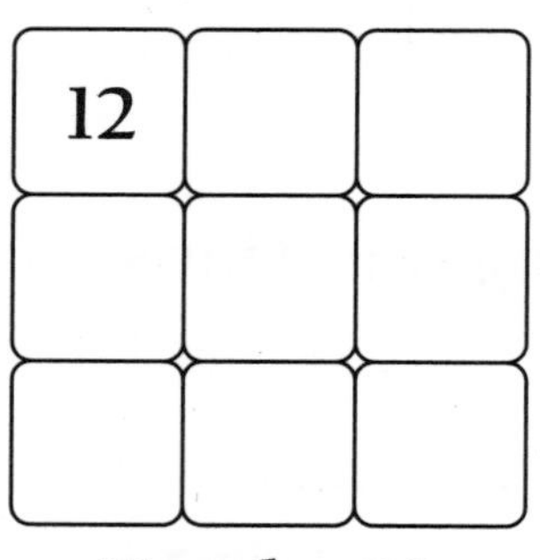

Total = 39

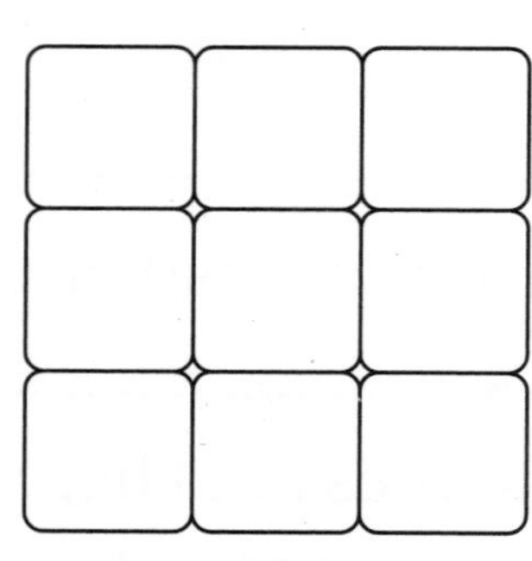

Total = 51

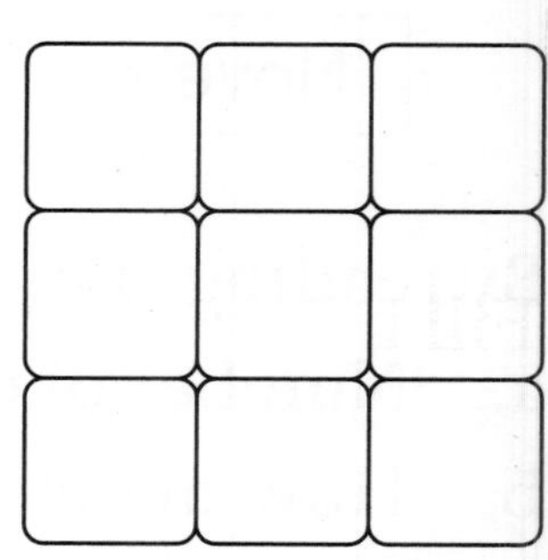

Total = 69

2. Make the factor tree.

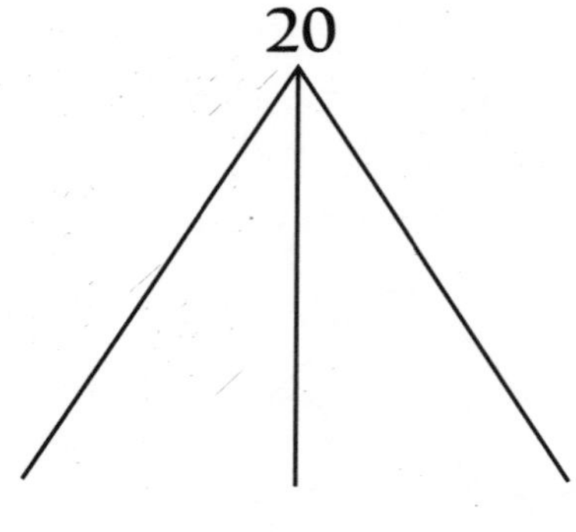

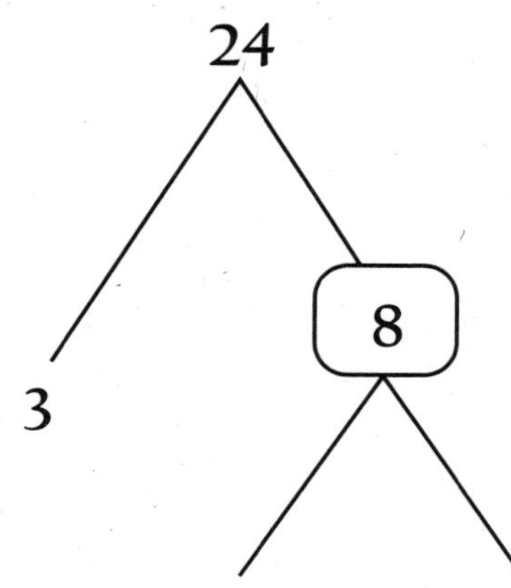

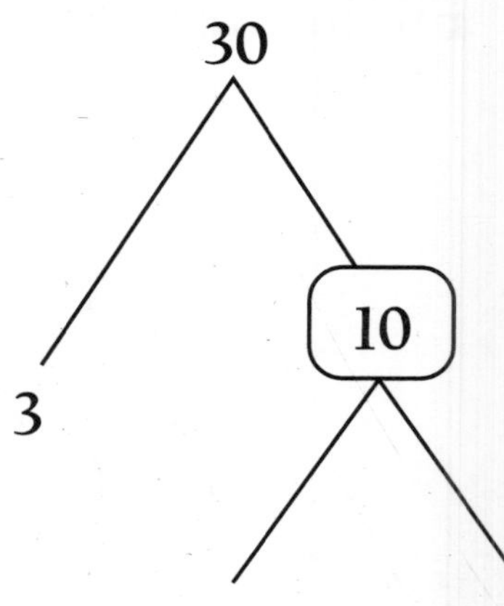

Grade

Patterns

Observe the pattern and fill in the empty space.

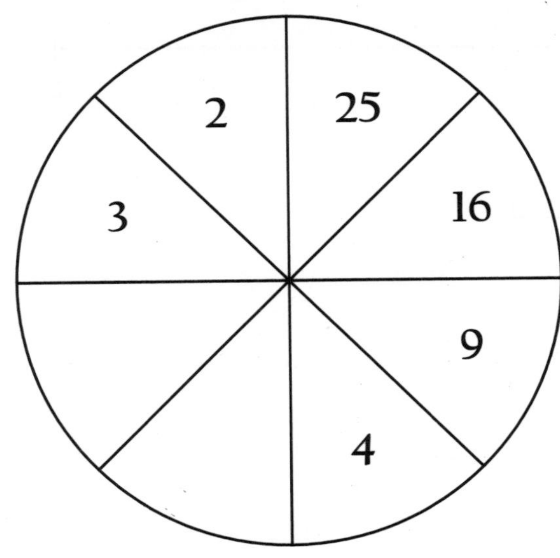

Fill in the boxes.

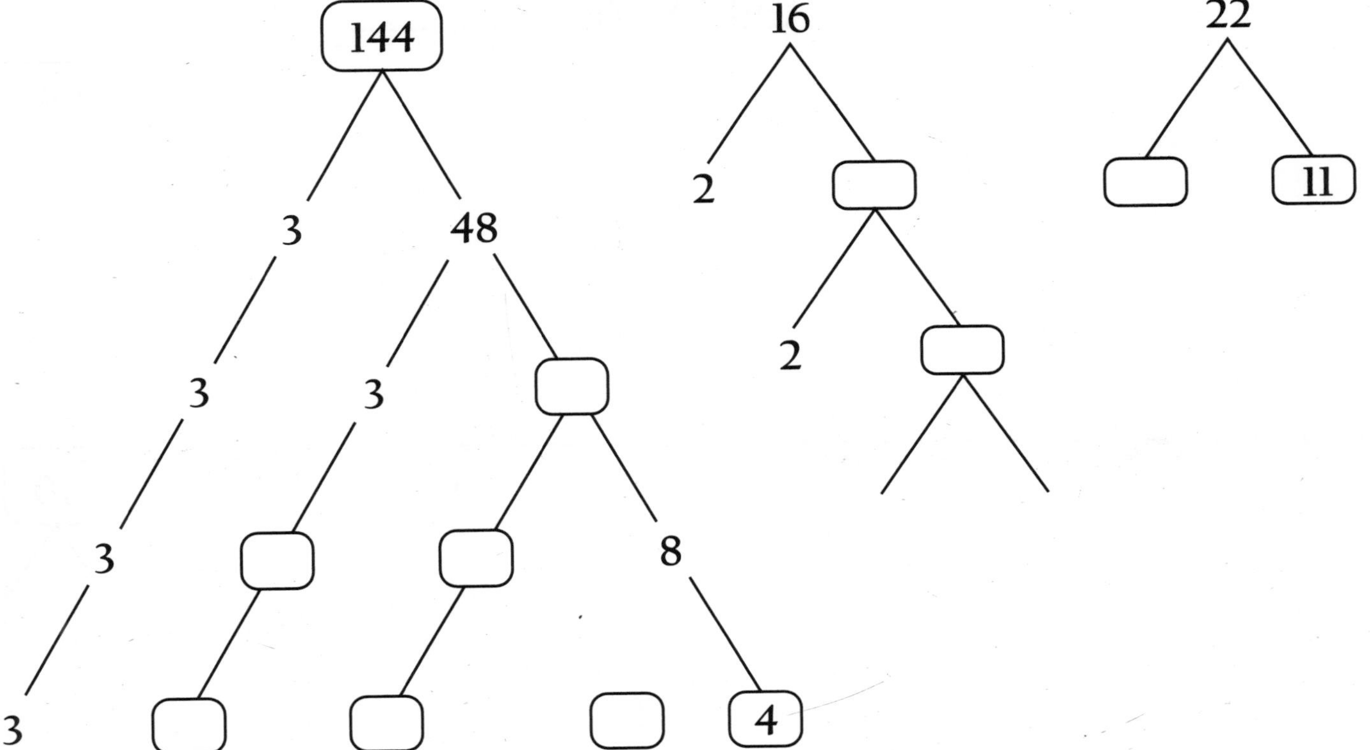

Grade ◯

Task 58

Geometry

1. Find the length of the following line segments.

a. a ———— b Ans. ....

b. c ———— d Ans. ....

c. e — f (i)

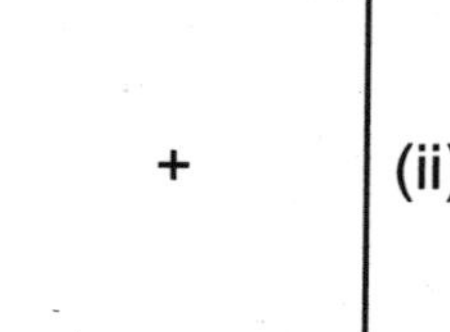

\+ g — h (ii)

Add (i) + (ii) ....

d.

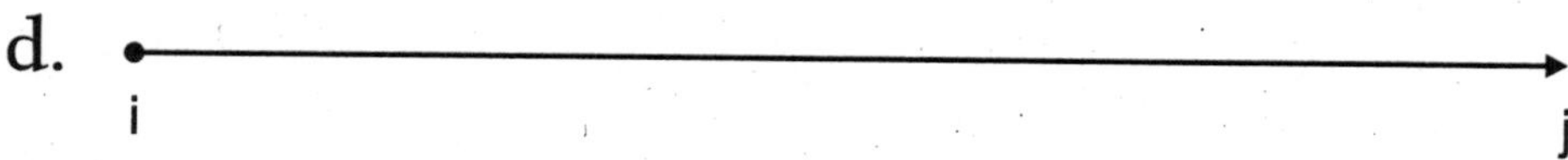

i ———→ j Ans. ....

e. k ———→ l Ans. ....

'rade

ore on geometry

Draw the line segments of the following measurements.

a. 13 cm

b. 5.4 cm

c. 6 cm

d. 8.5 cm

e. 6.4 cm

f. 7.2 cm

Draw the rays of given measurements.

a. 5.7 cm

b. 3.9 cm

c. 2.7 cm

d. 8.5 cm

e. 4.9 cm

Grade ◯

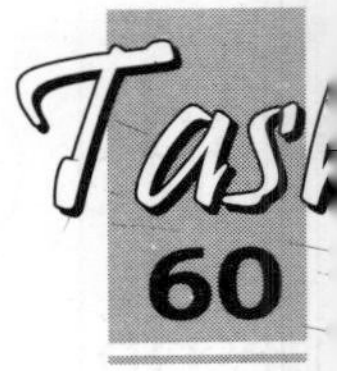

Perimeters

1. Find the perimeters.

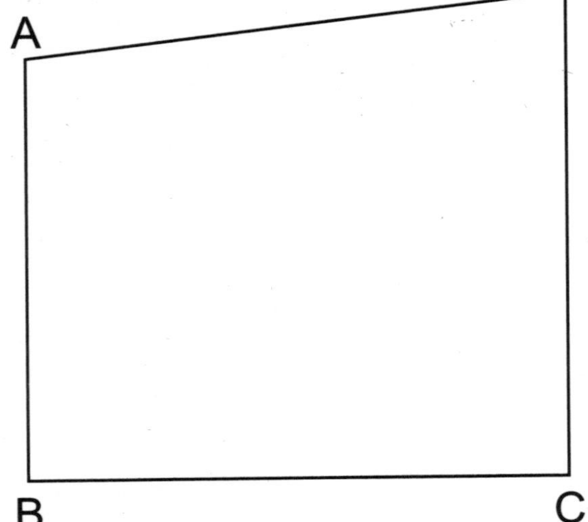

A
D
B
C

Perimeters

a. ....

b. ....

D
C
8 cm.
A
8 cm.
B

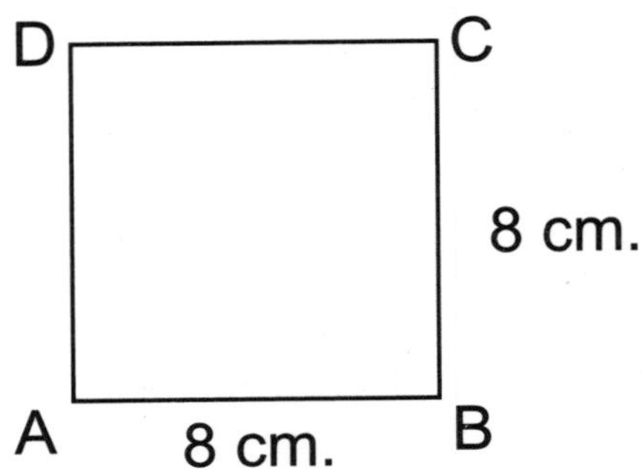

2. Match the figures having same perimeters.

4 cm.

4 cm.
4 cm.
4 cm.

3 cm.
3 cm.

3 cm.
4 cm.
2 cm.
4 cm.
3

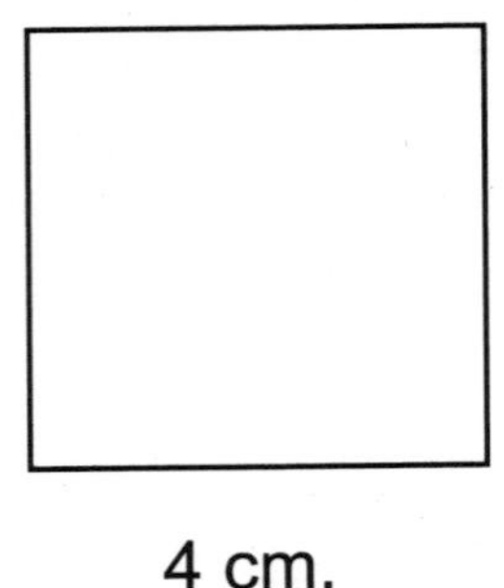

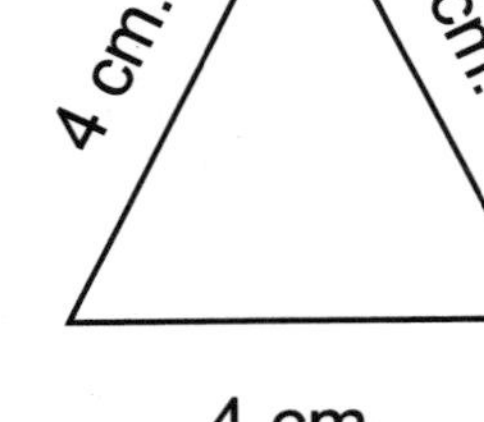

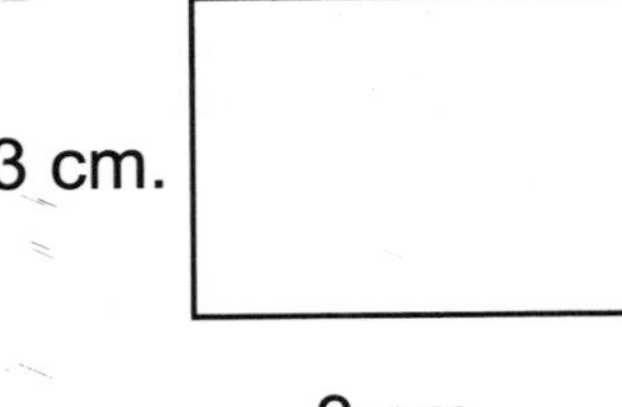

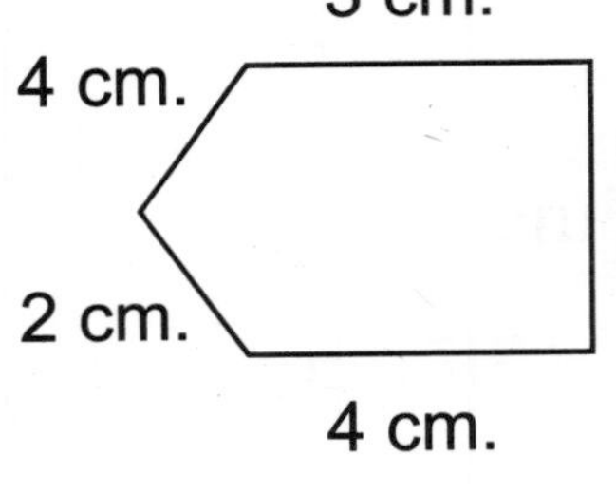

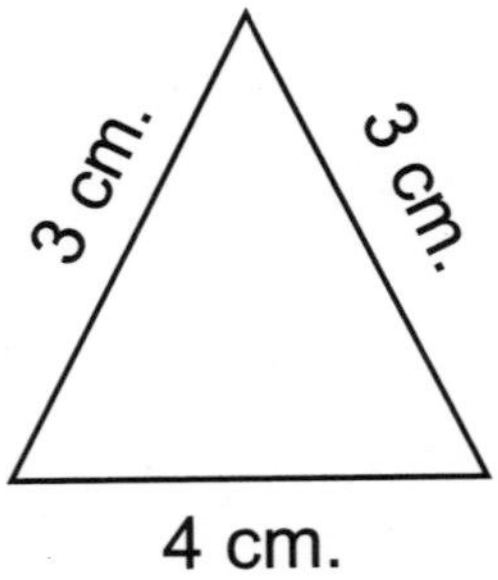

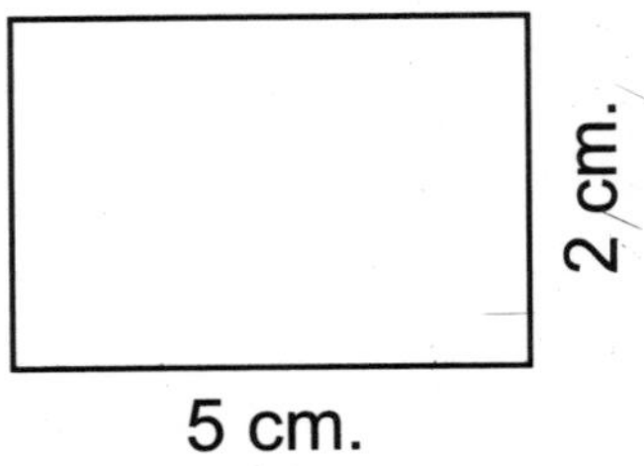

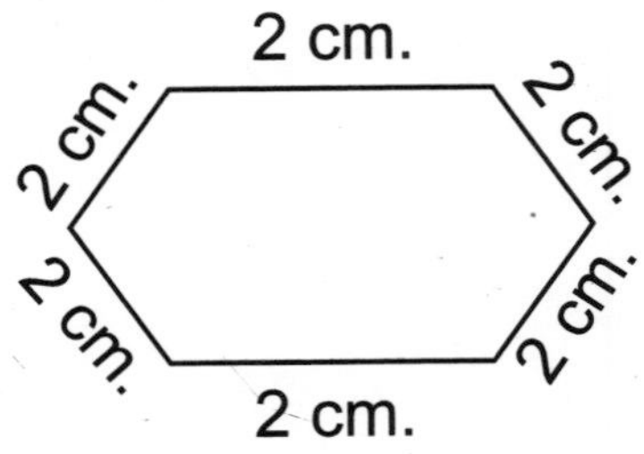

3 cm.
3 cm.
4 cm.

2 cm.
5 cm.

2 cm.
2 cm.
2 cm.
2 cm.
2 cm.
2 cm.

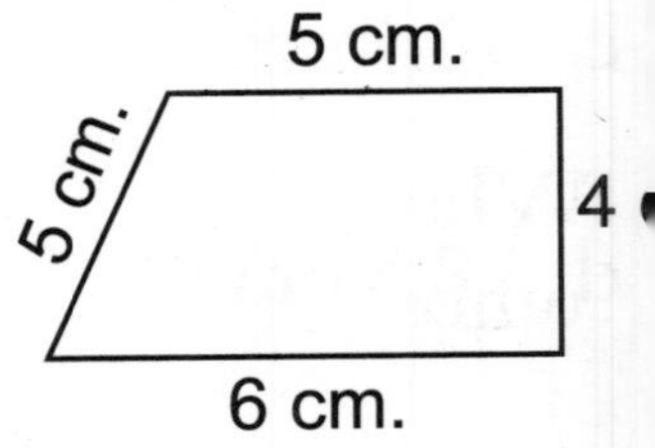

5 cm.
5 cm.
4
6 cm.

ɪrade ◯

uestions related to perimeter

A rectangular field is 150 m long and 125 m wide. Find the perimeter of the field.

Each side of a square is 2 m long. What will be its perimeter?

How much wire will be needed to fence a field 200 m long and 150 m wide?

What is the perimeter of a hexagon whose all the six sides are exactly equal and that is 6 cm 2 mm?

Find the side of a square whose perimeter is 452 m.

What is the perimeter of a triangle whose sides are 6, 7, and 9 cm each?

What is the perimeter of an equilateral triangle whose each side is 8 cm long?

Grade ◯

Angles

1. An angle less than 90^0 is called an .... angle.

2. x and y are called .... angles.

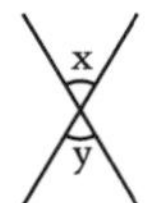

3. x and y are called .... angles.

4. x and y are called .... angles.

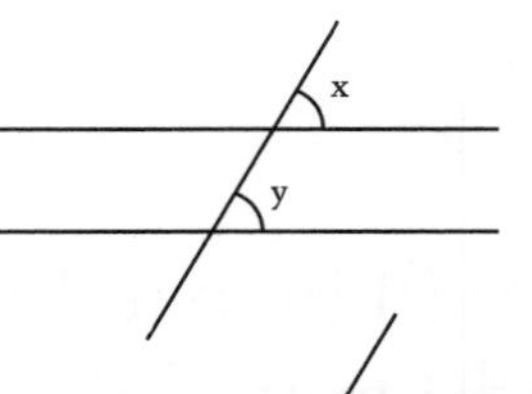

5. x and y are called .... angles.

6. A straight angle is one which has an angle of .... degrees.

7. A right angle is one which has an angle of .... degrees.

8. Make a reflex angle.

9. How many angles a triangle has? ....

10. How many angles a square has? ....

11. How many angles a pentagon has? ....

12. How many angles a hexagon has? ....

Grade ◯

nswer the following

Draw a triangle having all angles less than 90°

An equilateral triangle has all angles .... It is called scalene triangle.

An isosceles angle has two angles .... and two sides ....

A right triangle has one angle .... degrees.

The sum of three angles of a D is equal to .... degrees.

A triangle has three sides 13 cm, 11 cm and 14 cm.
What is its perimeter? ....

The sum of two sides of a triangles is more than the .... side.

The perimeter of a square is 60 cm, what is its side?

Name the rays shown in the figure?

....

O, A, B, C, D

. What is the perimeter of the pentagon with each side 5 cm.

A hexagon has .... side.

. An octagon has .... side.

Grade ◯

Task 64

Circles

1. Draw circles with radii in your notebook.

   a. 2.9 cm

   b. 4.0 cm

   c. 3.5 cm

   d. 5.0 cm

   e. 7.0 cm

2. If the radius of a circle is 12 cm, what is its diameter?

3. If the longest chord of a circle is 16 cm, what is its radius?

4. What is the circumference of a circle whose diameter is 7 cm?

5. Half of the circle is called a ....

6. What is the area of a circle? ....

7. The centre of a circle always lie .... of the circle.

8. Find the area of a circle whose radius is 14 cm. ....

9. What is area of a semi circle whose radius is 3.5 cm? ....

10. The radius of a wheel is 28 cm. How much distance it will cover in 10 revolutions?

rade

ore about circles

Draw circles of following diameters in your notebook.

a. 4.5 cm

b. 6 cm

c. 8 cm

d. 10 cm

e. 6.5 cm

. What is sector of a circle?

. Find the circumference of a circle whose diameter is 14 cm.

. The circumference of a bicycle wheel is 2 metres. How much distance it will cover in 150 revolutions?

. What is circumference of a pond whose diameter is 35 m?

. Diameter is the longest .... of the circle.

. What is the area of the quadrant of a circle whose radius is 14 cm?

. Wheels are of the shape of a ....

. How many quadrants are there in a circle?

Grade ◯

Misc. questions

1. Fill in the blanks.

a. [222 ☐ $\frac{8}{10}$] ☐ 110 = 221

b. 8 ☐ 6 + 4 ☐ 13 + 9 ☐ 100 = 1000

c. [666 ☐ 6] ☐ [100 ☐ 11] = 0

d. [5 ☐ 20] [7000 ☐ 7] [20 ☐ 30] = 500

2. Find L.C.M. of 4, 6, and 8= ....

3. Fill in the boxes.

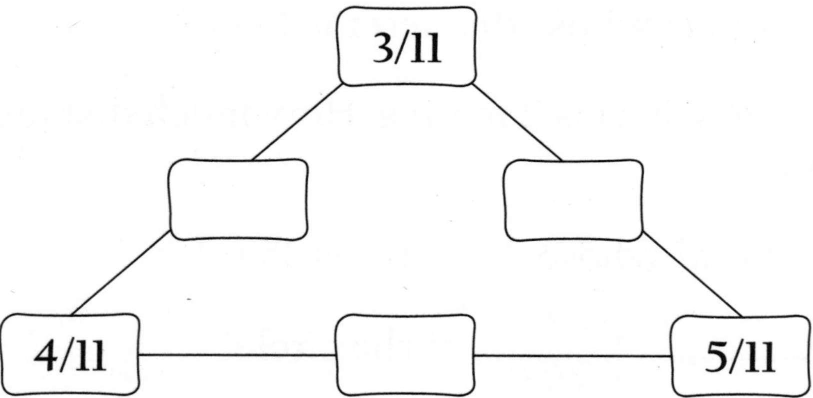

4. Polygons with 5 lines segments are ....

5. Twice the radius of a circle is ....

6. Half of 512 is ....

Grade ◯

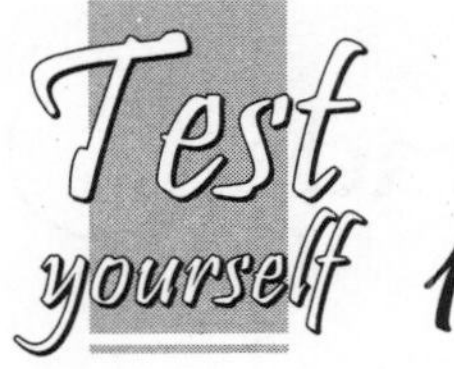

The numeral for eight thousand five hundred forty is ....

. Express 5019 in words ....

. 10 more then 1895 ....

. 100 more then 1735 ....

. 1875 = ... thousand .... hundreds .... tens .... ones

. 735 = ... thousand .... hundreds .... tens .... ones

. Arrange in descending order.

7321, 3721, 7212, 2137, 8725, 1925

....

. Arrange in ascending order.

5430, 9270, 5000, 9100, 2171, 2375

....

9. 875 × 100 = ...

10. The number of bananas in 2 dozen are ....

11. 117 ÷ 13 ....

12. Nine–eighth can be written as ....

13. 5/4 × 20 = ...

Grade ◯

Test yourself 2

1. The predecessor of 1179 = ...
2. The successor of 5469 is = ...
3. 18 × 7 = ...
4. 19 × 2 = ...
5. 120 ÷ 12 = ...
6. 500 × 15 = ...
7. The number of 20 paise coins in 5 rupees ....
8. 8750 paise = ... rupees .... paise.
9. If the cost of 8 tables is Rs. 4800, what is the cost of 1 table? ....
10. Write the numerals for the following in the Hindu–Arabic system.
    a. Fifty eight lakh eight thousand nine ....
    b. Seven crore four thousand eighty five ....
    c. Nine crore three hundred eight ....
11. Write the place value of 8 in the following numbers.
    a. 28754 ....
    b. 97800 ....
    c. 3854 ....
    d. 11873 ....
12. Write the following in words.
    a. 52573 ....
    b. 310003 ....
    c. 719203 ....

Grade ◯

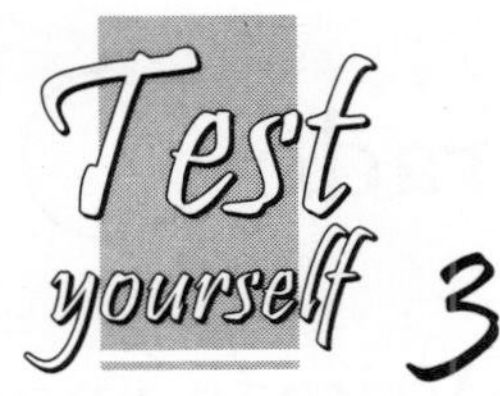

1. The Hindu–Arabic numeral for XXIV is ....
2. The Roman numeral for 84 = ...
3. 2354 + 1100 + 117 = ...
4. 6395 – 1170 = ...
5. 98 ÷ .... = 14
6. The factors of 54 are = ...
7. 819 ÷ 10 = ... quotient, ... remainder
8. One third of 18 = ...
9. 816 × 1000 = ...
10. 8000 ÷ 100 = ...
11. The fraction with 8 as numerator and 12 as denominator ....
12. 15m 11cm + 8m 10 cm = ... m .... cm
13. 82 Kg 40 g = ... g
14. The place value of 9 in 19732 is ....
15. DCLXX = ...
16. Write 514 in Roman ....
17. Write 312 in Roman ....
18. Add 5180 + 312 + 19 = ...
19. Subtract 8921 – 7232 = ...

Grade ◯

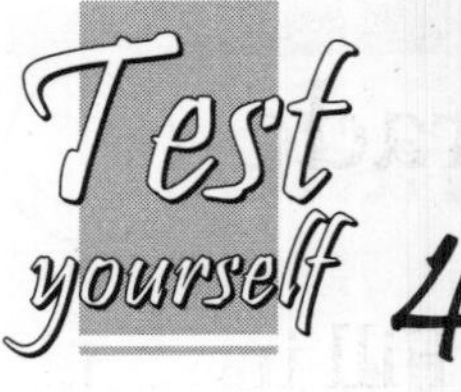

1. Write in numerals.

a. Nine lakh five thousand eighty four ....

b. Seventy seven lakh ninety eight ....

c. Fifty lakh eighteen ....

d. Seven lakh seven thousand one hundred three ....

e. Eight lakh seventy thousand five hundred sixty nine. ....

2. Solve the following sums.

a. 800000 + 7000 + 80 + 4 = ...

b. 90000 + 10 = ...

c. 600000 + 400 + 5 = ...

d. 140000 + 8000 + 100 = ...

e. 600000 + 60000 + 4000 + 500 + 19 = ...

3. Put in >, < or =.

1.12	☐	2.3	$\frac{91}{100}$	☐	$\frac{12}{10}$
5.10	☐	1.70	$\frac{52}{100}$	☐	$\frac{52}{10}$
7.3	☐	9.10	$1\frac{2}{10}$	☐	$2\frac{3}{100}$
1.10	☐	1.1	$\frac{19}{100}$	☐	$\frac{21}{100}$
5.12	☐	5.20			
1.00	☐	1.00			
3.25	☐	3.15			

Grade ◯

Test yourself 5

Fill in the blanks.

a. The successor of 92154 = ...

b. The successor of 10099 = ...

c. The predecessor of 8170 = ...

d. The predecessor of 769990 = ...

e. The successor of 54681 = ...

Solve the following.

a. 56945 ÷ 1000 = ... quotient .... remainder

b. .... ÷ 962 = 1

c. .... × 4162 = 0

d. 542 ÷ 542 = ...

e. 84 × 7 × 0 = ...

f. 299 ÷ 10 = quotient .... remainder ....

g. 351 ÷ 20 = quotient .... remainder ....

Encircle the greatest number.

a. 15279, 132945, 7287, 74329, 119200

b. 112325, 197321, 45432, 928732, 41254

c. 523215, 321521, 987321, 532115, 567892

Encircle the smallest number.

a. 54324, 27392, 54382, 1179800, 100011

b. 91721, 519327, 211937, 354321, 1179000

c. 9912, 3152, 1253, 5525, 57225

Grade ◯

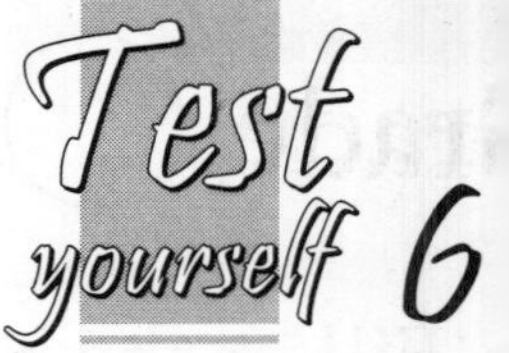

1. Write E for even and O for odd numerals.

a.	98	b.	192 ....
c.	112	d.	115 ....
e.	115	f.	420 ....
g.	77	h.	24 ....
i.	183	j.	29 ....
k.	110	l.	32 ....

2. Write even number between 71 and 85.

....

3. Write odd number between 21 and 35.

....

4. Write first five multiples of 9.

....

5. Write first five multiples of 15.

....

6. The smallest even number of three digit is ....
7. The smallest odd number of four digit is ....
8. Write all the factors of:
   a. 36 ....
   b. 48 ....
   c. 100 ....
   d. 125 ....
   e. 75 ....
9. What are the common factors of 24 and 48? ....
10. What are common factors of 8 and 32? ....

Date :......................

Teacher's Signature :..................

Grade ◯

7

Find the perimeters of rectangles having the following sides.

a. Length=8 m, Breadth=7 m

b. Length=12 m, Breadth=8 m

Find the perimeters of the triangles having the following sides.

a. 5 cm, 3 cm and 3 cm

b. 8 cm, 19 cm and 15 cm

c. 3 cm, 4 cm and 5 cm

Write the time.

a. 2 hours after 6 O' clock ....

b. 4 hours after 7 O' clock ....

c. 2 hours before 3.30 A.M. ....

d. 1 hour after 5.30 P.M. ....

e. 2 hours after 9.00 A.M. ....

f. 7 hours after 3 o clock ....

. Fill in the blanks.

a. 1.5 hours = ... minutes

b. 5 hours= .... minutes

c. 3 days= .... hours

d. 5 weeks = ... days

e. ¾ of 2 hours = ... minutes

f. 40 minute = ... seconds

Date :......................

Teacher's Signature :........................

Grade ◯

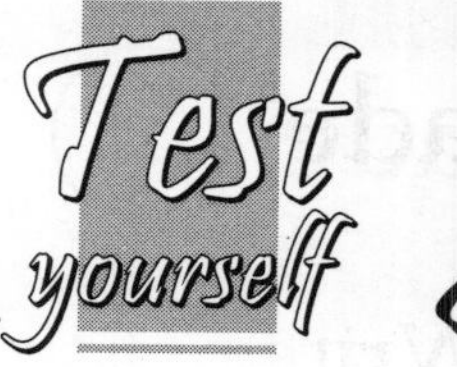

1. Fill in the blanks.

$\frac{8}{2} = \frac{40}{\square}$ $\qquad$ $\frac{7}{4} = \frac{\square}{28}$

$\frac{9}{5} = \frac{\square}{40}$ $\qquad$ $\frac{7}{9} = \frac{49}{\square}$

$\frac{3}{10} = \frac{18}{\square}$ $\qquad$ $\frac{8}{4} = \frac{\square}{28}$

2. Fill in the boxes < or >

$\frac{8}{5} \square \frac{9}{5}$ $\qquad$ $\frac{9}{7} \square \frac{4}{2}$

$\frac{3}{8} \square \frac{3}{9}$ $\qquad$ $\frac{5}{8} \square \frac{6}{9}$

$\frac{7}{5} \square \frac{10}{7}$ $\qquad$ $\frac{5}{8} \square \frac{5}{9}$

3. Arrange the following in ascending order.

$\frac{5}{9} \quad \frac{3}{9} \quad \frac{8}{9} \quad \frac{7}{9} \quad \frac{15}{9}$

$\frac{1}{2} \quad \frac{2}{7} \quad \frac{5}{4} \quad \frac{1}{2} \quad \frac{1}{8}$

4. Arrange the following in descending order.

$\frac{1}{5} \quad \frac{1}{7} \quad \frac{1}{2} \quad \frac{1}{9} \quad \frac{1}{3}$

$\frac{4}{2} \quad \frac{7}{3} \quad \frac{5}{4} \quad \frac{3}{2} \quad \frac{1}{5}$

Date :.................... $\qquad$ Teacher's Signature :....................

rade ◯

Write the fractional numbers for the following.

7.5 = —

9.8 = —

8.34 = —

4.79 = —

1.71 = —

3.54 = —

2.2 = —

5.25 = —

Write in the decimal form.

$\frac{5}{10}$ = ...

$\frac{8}{2}$ = ...

$\frac{71}{100}$ = ...

$1\frac{3}{10}$ = ...

$\frac{54}{100}$ = ...

$2\frac{51}{100}$ = ...

$\frac{32}{100}$ = ...

$3\frac{1}{10}$ = ...

Write the following figures in words.

6.48 = ...

5.33 = ...

19.71 = ...

6.28 = ...

3.08 = ...

3.25 = ...

Write in expanded form.

4.97 = ...

13.52 = ...

58.73 = ...

Grade ◯

Test yourself 10

1. In the given pair of fractions mark (✓) for those which are equal and mark (×) for unequal.

$\frac{3}{2}$ and $\frac{5}{2}$ $\frac{2}{3}$ and $\frac{4}{6}$

$\frac{4}{5}$ and $\frac{5}{4}$ $\frac{5}{10}$ and $\frac{1}{2}$

$\frac{3}{6}$ and $\frac{4}{8}$ $\frac{5}{2}$ and $\frac{10}{4}$

$\frac{3}{5}$ and $\frac{6}{10}$ $\frac{5}{7}$ and $\frac{20}{28}$

2. Write the lowest form.

$\frac{80}{72}$ = ... $\frac{81}{27}$ = ... $\frac{121}{11}$ = ...

$\frac{56}{8}$ = ... $\frac{149}{151}$. = ... $\frac{175}{100}$ = ...

$\frac{124}{4}$ = ... $\frac{196}{\ }$ = ... $\frac{120}{10}$ = ...

3. Write in ascending order.

5.32, 8.12, 5.10, 5.01, 8.2 ....

3.25, 4.12, 4.7, 8.3, 9.2 ....

7.32, 5.1, 7.10, 3.20, 7.3 ....

6.12, 5.7, 8.7, 3.25, 7.25 ....

6.77, 6.71, 6.17, 6.07, 6.7 ....

7.11, 7.1, 7.4, 7.3, 7.6 ....

Date : 7/11/19   Teacher's Signature :..................